Blood Beyond the Keyhole

A Thrilling Teenage Adventure Story

by Colin Vard

Celtpress Ltd.

Celtpress Ltd.
Kindlestown Hill
Delgany
Co. Wicklow
Republic of Ireland
Tel/Fax: (01) 287 3026

ISBN 1-897973-01-2

Printed by Vision Print
Unit 3, Blackrock Business Centre
Brookfield Terrace
Blackrock, Co. Dublin

I would like to thank the following, without whose
invaluable help the publication of this book would not have
been possible:

Tony Kew, Richard Fox and Ciar

*This book is dedicated to Dáire and all the women who,
during the course of Irish history, acquitted themselves with
bravery and self-sacrifice in search of independence.*

Illustrations by Tony Kew

proclaimed the sign straddling the impressive wrought iron entrance gates. It was a miserable, grey September evening. The swiftly falling sea mist enveloped the driveway, so eloquently described as "manicured" in the school brochure. On and on we drove, the car's wheels spinning in the deep gravel. Past the tennis courts on the left, the running track on the right and on to the all-weather hockey pitch, which warranted no more than a momentary glance.

"Let it be made quite clear ...," I mumbled to an imaginary games master, "There is no way I am going to be subjected to the winter misery of galloping aimlessly around a wet and muddy north Wicklow field, trying to put a stupid lump of cork into a net."

No, a blazing log fire, a cup of hot chocolate and a toasted muffin smothered in fresh salted butter and jam made from sun-ripened fruits nurtured and plucked by the tender hands of the novice nuns.

Dad irritatingly drummed his fingers on the steering wheel.

Gustav, or Gus as he is better known, is a fashion agent and admits to being thirty-nine years old. He is very proud of his Polish ancestry. Grandad, Jacob, was born in Gdansk. He landed on Dublin docks in the early thirties. He was a furrier by trade. Soon after he arrived he met, fell in love with and married Grandma, Catherine, who at the time was working for the Red Cross.

Mum, Úna, a little younger than Dad, harbours a passion for horses. She works part time in a riding stables in Ashford and considers horse excrement to be not alone odourless but organic. To me it is simply another form of smelly animal dung. There is, of course, another side to Mum that is considerably more refined and willingly abandons these earthy outdoor pursuits and brings her to trendy Senõr Sassi's restaurant in Leeson Street. The muckers and cord jodhpurs replaced by a very revealing off the shoulder black dress. What a transformation! It is hard to believe that this stunningly beautiful and vivacious woman, making some final adjustments in front of the mirror, is the same woman who, a few hours previously, was seen merrily washing a horse's orifice. A few glasses of her favourite Chablis always helps her forget the call of the land. Mum and Dad courted Sassi's regularly.

As we rounded yet another corner, I was expecting a border post manned by a grizzly bunch of mercenary nuns. It was then I caught my first clear view of Mountclare. It struck me that this moment would be indelibly etched on my memory.

"Look at your new uniform!" screeched Mum. "It's covered in chocolate fudge ice cream."

She turned to Dad and said indignantly, "Not one of your better ideas?"

I meekly pointed out that it was an accident, but this had little effect. Mum scowled.

Dad brought the car to a halt close to the stone steps leading to the entrance porch. Mum frantically rubbed my tunic. Three emotions vied for my attention: excitement, apprehension and, most of all, pure undiluted fear! Finally the dreaded moment had arrived

"Come on, Gráinne," shouted Dad. "Her tunic is fine Úna!"

Mum frowned, squeezed my hand and smiled. "It will have to do," she said.

Dad waited on the first step carrying my suitcases. Síle, my younger sister with whom I had been engaged in various forms of guerilla warfare for almost ten years, chose this inopportune moment to ease a tear from the corner of her eye. Damn her. I thought I could rely on Síle to maintain her composure and not succumb to emotion.

It reminded me of Grandad's funeral. We had managed to contain our emotions all day, that is until we arrived at the grave side. A friend of Dad's came forward to offer his condolences and inexplicably broke down in tears. The strangest thing about this little man, who hailed from the North of Ireland, was that he had never even met Grandad. You could always rely on him, Dad said afterwards, to produce a sufficient amount of remorse at funerals. He was affectionately known where he worked as the Company Crier. Here he was, on cue, large salty tears streaming down his rosy cheeks. What had been a controlled and dignified Jewish funeral now resembled a prayer meeting of the faithful at the wailing wall in Jerusalem.

Dad struggled up the remaining steps and disappeared through the huge Gothic-style entrance doors. We made our way down the long corridor to the registration office. Dad's cowboy boots clicked noisily on the tiled floors, the weight of the suitcases severely hampering his forward motion, evidenced by the large beads of sweat appearing on his forehead and behind his ears. He mumbled something about Himalayan pack mules being treated more humanely. Education, he lectured, was very important, and this was a great opportunity to fulfil my ambition to become a solicitor. In fact his friend Bill, who ran an important legal office in Fitzwilliam Street in Dublin, had promised me a position when I qualified. I recalled one of Dad's jokes: What is black and brown and looks good on a solicitor? ... a Doberman! The joke always made me laugh.

Mum and I registered while Dad and Síle viewed the old school photos lining the walls from the refectory to the registration office. They must have found an old photo of Mum as we could hear them laughing hysterically at the far end of the corridor. This prompted Mum to scuttle off in the opposite direction. The registration completed and the laughter abated, I nervously followed a senior prefect out into the darkness and across the courtyard to the coach house that was to be my surrogate home for the next six years. It appeared that we had to spend a year in the wilderness being cleansed before being admitted in to the inner sanctum of the main school building.

We climbed the narrow rickety stairs to the first year dormitory and were welcomed by a young nun who introduced herself as Sister Clodagh. I cannot recall unpacking, making my bed or walking back across the courtyard to the main building. I do, however, remember walking into the recreation room. In fact, I will never forget it as long as I live. It was an overwhelming experience. Within this aural nightmare over two hundred girls were hugging, kissing and crying in an unbridled frenzy. A few of the first years unfortunately wailed in despair. Mum and Dad, who had been introduced to the teachers, were now having a rather intense conversation with Sister Clodagh in the bay window. As they bade farewell, Dad offered his hand to Sister Clodagh. She took it warmly and held it while she kissed him on the cheek. Mum, momentarily isolated, turned to Síle and I, smiled nervously, and walked towards us, head bowed. When she was within a couple of feet, I noticed that her mascara was running. She had been crying. I would have yielded also except for the timely intervention of two other first years who introduced themselves as Eimear and Siobhan.

After hugs and kisses and, thankfully, a tearless farewell Mum, Dad and Síle headed back to Dublin. Eimear, Siobhan and I were led back to the dormitory by Sister Clodagh. We talked for hours with the other girls who made up the first year until Sister Clodagh reappeared in the doorway and instructed us in no uncertain terms to prepare ourselves for sleep .The lights would be turned off in five minutes! We duly washed, undressed and jumped into bed. It was a strange feeling lying in the dark, alone except for my thoughts. For the first time I was without the strength of my father, the gentle reassurances of my mother and the sibling rivalry of my sister, Síle.

CHAPTER 2

I awoke early. It was still dark. Through force of habit I turned to switch on my radio but, of course, I was not at home. Mentally - yes, physically - no. I thought of Honey, my Yorkshire terrier. Dad would be heading out to the gym now. He let Honey out for a run at this time every weekday. The mischievous rascal always managed to sneak up to my bedroom while Dad made Mum a cup of tea. Honey would jump up on the bed, dive under the blankets and wait until he heard Dad's car going down the driveway before resurfacing briefly to smother my face in wet licks. Exhausted, he would return under the covers, his cold and wet snout neatly positioned against the warm flesh exposed between the tops and bottoms of my pyjamas. What will he do this morning when he realises I'm not there?, I thought.

I don't know how long I lay there feeling sorry for myself. It seemed like hours, but it may only have been minutes. I sat up and observed my two new friends, Eimear and Siobhan, sleeping soundly on the other side of the dormitory. I did not know them very long, but it was easy to see that they were two very different people indeed. Eimear was very tall, painfully shy, with the palest complexion I had ever seen. Her dad William, a little chubby balding man, came from an old farming family in Monasterboice just outside Drogheda. They lived in a lovely house built on a plot of land her grandad gave them. William broke the family tradition, abandoned the soil and went to work in a clothing factory in Tallaght making ladies underwear. He was a sports fanatic and quite obviously a Manchester United supporter. I gathered this from the subtle clues he displayed when he came to visit Eimear. The ghastly full length red and black striped duvet coat. Summer and winter he wore this coat matched with an equally garish scarf with "Red Devils" emblazoned on it. His four wheel drive Patrol was also in the Manchester United colours. He had to buy a Patrol as apparently it was the only road going vehicle sold in Europe with red and white paint work. In total contrast, her mother Jenny was a nurse and worked in the tropical disease department of the Lourdes hospital in Drogheda, which probably goes a long way to explaining her tolerance of her father's illness. She was an attractive dark-haired woman who had little time for sport. Jenny buried herself in the local drama society and actually auditioned for the part of Scarlett O'Hara on the Late Late Show. She claimed that after the auditions Gaybo told her over a glass of wine that, in his not-so-humble opinion, she was the most accomplished amateur actress he had encountered in years. She failed to get the part.

Siobhan was the complete opposite to Eimear. She was small, dark and blamed her dumpy figure and sallow complexion on her second generation Italian parents. .She was very outgoing, which was understandable being the youngest of eight children who worked in their parents' "restaurant" in New Ross. Her initial description of their restaurant was, we subsequently found out, bending the truth a little. In reality, it was a fish and chip shop. When this fact became public knowledge Siobhan, to her credit, had to endure more than her fair share of ribbing, especially in the refectory.

"Hey Siobhan. You wanta that I passa da salt n veenneger?"

I buried my head in the pillow, closed my eyes and drifted. I was at the R.D.S., my arms outstretched to accept the Aga Khan trophy on behalf of the victorious Irish Show Jumping team. Paul Darragh was smiling as President Robinson complimented me on my outstanding double clear, when I was jolted from my slumber by Sister Clodagh's hand pulling me out of bed.

"Come on Gráinne, time to get up. Anybody not dressed when I return will have a lovely cold shower tonight!"

I'd swear I heard her say "Make my day, punks" as she went out the door. I struggled out of bed and instead of being greeted by the warmth of my sheepskin rug, my senses were scattered by the ice cold, marble-coloured lino. Hopping from foot to foot, I washed and dressed considerably quicker than I would have done at home. The absence of mirrors over the antiquated porcelain sinks eliminated the need for Spot Patrol. Now the only opportunity to inspect new species of spots or blackheads would be restricted to the only mirror in the room, which was communal. Too long spent inspecting at this mirror was bad publicity.

Sister Clodagh re-appeared and requested us to gather round. She was a tall, elegant and very beautiful woman. She would have been about Mum's age, I thought. Suddenly it struck me. This must be the nun I overheard Mum and Dad talking about last Christmas on the way to Schull.

We had been driving for hours, Síle dozed contentedly beside me in the back of the car, her Walkman irritatingly banging and crashing. Dad was listening to and laughing at a B.B.C. Radio special on American comedian Andrew Dice Clay. Mum had been sleeping soundly since we left Dublin. She claimed that she was nursing a menstrual-related headache. Much to Mum's annoyance, Andrew began to recite some alternative versions of well-known children's nursery rhymes. She sat forward demanding that the station should be changed or the radio turned off. Dad objected and did neither but just turned the volume down a little. Mum now chose her words less carefully and the

8

radio was silenced.

As the Rock of Cashel appeared, Dad turned to Mum and said, "Do you realise it's almost twenty years since we sold Javelin here at the Rock Horse Sales. I often wonder whatever happened to her. I suppose she must be dead now. Wasn't that the day the wheel fell off the horse box Kevin lent us?"

Mum shifted position and replied angrily, "How could you forget what happened that day?"

She continued, in a quieter voice, "If the priest from Mountclare, Father Kirkpatrick, hadn't noticed the wheel rolling into the ditch and returned it to you in the Castle car park, you would have had some explaining to do to Kevin when we returned that night! How could you have driven over two miles and not notice that one of the wheels had fallen off the horse box? I wish we had never invited Clodagh to the horse sales. If she hadn't met Father Kirkpatrick that day, she would surely have continued her studies in Trinity."

Dad sighed in acknowledgement.

I was a little confused, but enthralled. I noticed Síle's Walkman, like Mum, had fallen silent. Dad smiled sympathetically. Mum didn't respond. I could see in the vanity mirror she was not asleep but deep in thought and clearly upset. After a few moments, she sat forward and looked over her shoulder to check if Síle and I were asleep. I closed my eyes quickly. Reassured, Mum continued.

"Gus, what were the chances of Clodagh and Father Kirkpatrick crossing paths six years later to the very day he officiated at Róisín's memorial service? It's unbelievable. What on earth did they speak about that day that made Clodagh abandon her studies and return to Mountclare as a novice nun? The fact that Róisín's body was never found only adds to the mystery. How could you ever come to terms with the fact that your thirteen-year-old twin sister disappears into thin air? I remember clearly, Clodagh left Mountclare on the junior hockey team coach at nine a.m.. She waved good-bye to Róisín, who was in the infirmary, and returned at eight p.m. that same night proudly cradling the Leinster Junior Hockey Cup. I can still see Clodagh grabbing the cup, sprinting across the courtyard and disappearing up the stairs to the infirmary. Róisín could not be found anywhere. Matron thought she had sneaked out and travelled to Dublin with the team. The following weeks were awful. The memorial service was heart-breaking. It was weird burying and praying over an empty coffin. The official Garda report was that Róisín must have gone for a walk, fallen into the marshes, drowned and her body swept out to sea."

I was miles away and only came back to reality when Eimear dug her elbow painfully into my ribs. Before I had a chance to exact some form of revenge, Sister Clodagh turned on her heels and headed down the stairs to the courtyard.

We dived down the rickety stairs, as always in single file, skipped across the courtyard and passed through the side door into the main building

My eyes had almost adjusted to the dark when I realised that Sister Clodagh and most of the girls had disappeared around the next corner. I stopped for a moment and noticed that one of the doors in the passage was ajar, so I had a look inside. It was a sitting room with a sofa bed in the corner, which was odd because I thought all the nuns, except for matron who had a room off the infirmary, slept in the main building. As I left the room I noted that there was another door, much older, directly opposite. I dropped to my knees to have a look through the key hole, but I could see nothing.

"Gráinne! what in the name of God are you doing?"

I looked up. It was Sister Clodagh.

"The door was open and, and, I just, just wondered what was in the room, and ... and as I came out I noticed, ... I'm sorry Sister."

"This is my room and it is strictly out of bounds."

Sister Clodagh produced a bunch of keys from her pocket and locked her door. Pointing to the older door opposite she said, "This door leads nowhere, Gráinne. Contrary to school folklore, there is no secret room or passageway behind the door, just a stone wall, and certainly no women wailing and scratching at the walls trying to get out at night."

"Yes Sister," I said quite meekly as she beckoned me to follow her down the passage.

Dad went to Clongowes, a boarding school in Kildare. He often spoke about a secret room they had in the Castle tower. The room had no doors or windows either. On the same night every year a black hearse drawn by six white horses appeared at the gate lodge at midnight. A headless coachman then drove the coach at great speed up the gravelled driveway to the main castle door. Another man, a soldier wielding a long sword, jumped from the coach, ran through the solid oak doors and up the stairs into this secret room where he was heard to call out a woman's name. He then fell on his sword while the woman screamed hysterically.

We caught up with the others in the main hall. I watched in amazement as Sister Clodagh bounded up the stairs three at a time, not at all lady-like, I thought, never mind nun-like. We followed and, depending on our level of fitness, chose one or two steps at a time. Poor Siobhan went for the last three at the top, failed miserably and ended up face down on the landing.

After inspecting the second years' decidedly higher standard of accommodation, we made our way back down the beautifully carved hardwood staircase and on past the nuns' recreation room. Having learnt my lesson earlier, I ignored the open door and, like everyone else, headed for the chapel. The students' recreation room was enormous, with polished wooden floors and a huge bow window draped with a moth-eaten green velvet curtain. It overlooked the entrance porch on one side and the main car park on the other. There was a motley assortment of tables and chairs sprinkled at random around the room. Some of the tables had chess sets, others draughts. All had notices demanding that:

Under no circumstances should any school property be removed from this room.

In the corner sat a relic of a television. Thirty wooden chairs set five deep formed a half circle around the set. We followed Sister Clodagh further down the corridor until we reached two large and ornate wooden doors.

Sister Clodagh opened the doors and, with her index finger placed across her lips, ushered us into the Chapel. It was apparent that while we were on tour the rest of the school had been celebrating their first mass of the new term. The school turned in unison as we were ushered in. We were viewed with disdain and mirth.

"Right girls, out you go!" whispered Sister Clodagh as she nodded apologetically to the priest whose uplifting sermon we had interrupted.

In the refectory, we were greeted by Sister Ignatius, a jolly Italian woman as broad as she was long, a real "mama" in nun's clothing.

We were split up and directed to our respective tables.

Sister Ignatius explained that each table had one girl from each year and four tables made up what was called a "house". There were ten houses in all. The relative calm was disturbed by the arrival of the sixth years, who strutted in confidently. Most did not look at all like school girls but rather like secretaries and solicitors. Each proudly took her place at the head of her table. Maureen, or Mo, was head of our table and was, like most of the girls, very friendly. We chatted freely and within minutes I felt I had known her for years. Her dad, Jonathan, was a novelist and principal of a national school in Portlaoise. When I met him first I got quite a shock. He looked like of one of those new-age hippies. As it turned out, he was an old friend of Dad's and the reason for his odd attire was actually quite logical. In June 1970, when all good hippies had hung up their flares, Jonathan, on his annual pilgrimage to London, visited the Mecca of hippie clothing shops, Carnaby Street, and came across a trader selling off flared denim jeans and desert boots. Never known to be a slave to fashion or, more importantly, to miss a bargain, he bought six pairs of jeans and five pairs of boots for twenty pounds. According to Mo, he still had two pairs of unworn jeans and boots buried in his wardrobe.

The remainder of the girls arrived from morning prayers and made their way to their respective tables. As quickly as the noise level had increased, it decreased due to the arrival of school principal, Mother Mary. As if by magic, the refectory instantly fell silent as she glided to her podium without a single word or gesture. I was in awe.

Mother Mary climbed the podium and stood watching us for a few moments. She took a deep breath and launched into a ten minute tonic for the troops. I found her enthusiasm infectious. The speech and subsequent prayers completed, the refectory filled with frantic conversation and the wonderful aroma of fried food. After twenty minutes of feverish ingestion and conversation, Mother Mary made her way back to the podium. Mo informed me that the school council was about to be announced. I glanced around the room and noted the animated expressions etched on the sixth years' faces. It was indeed a great honour to be elected to the council. Mother Mary welcomed the first years, smiled, opened her diary and announced to squeals of excitement and moans of disappointment the names of the various prefects. When she finally announced that Mo had been selected as head girl, the refectory erupted as the girls in unison jumped to their feet and applauded. It was obvious that Mo was a very popular choice.

After lunch, which like breakfast was a gastronomic delight, Matron spoke to us about personal hygiene as well as more mundane problems, like how to brush your teeth, hair and shoes, then informed us that we were free to make our own plans for the remainder of the afternoon. It was a lovely day so Eimear, Siobhan, and I decided to go for a swim in the outside pool. We never thought to question if it was heated. Luckily, it was. We ducked and dived all afternoon and would be there still only an aggrieved Sister Clodagh appeared, complaining bitterly that she had just spent the last hour searching for us. She demanded that we remove our wrinkled skin from the pool, dress and report immediately to the refectory for tea. We arrived in the refectory over ten minutes late. Mother Mary was distinctly perturbed by our intrusion.

Seated at the end of the table, I ate in silence. I was famished, but I was also trying to come to terms with Sister Clodagh's predicament. Twenty years ago her thirteen-year-old twin sister disappears. Her body is never found. Six years later to the day, she has a chance meeting with the same priest who officiated at Róisín's memorial service.

After a long conversation with the priest, she abandons university and returns to Mountclare as a novice nun. Sister Clodagh's living quarters are for some inexplicable reason isolated from the main building and opposite a room supposedly haunted by a wailing woman and with no apparent access.

After supper, we headed off to the gymnasium to meet our respective house captains. It all sounded very exciting and I put my name down for hockey, tennis, volleyball, cross country running and even chess! It was very difficult not to be caught up in the excitement. The system was that throughout the year each house would compete in various sports and academic contests, which the following June would culminate in the winning house being crowned champions. Suddenly, I realised to my horror that I was the only first year present. It was after ten o' clock - I should be in the dormitory. I ran blindly all the way down the corridors, my footsteps echoing noisily on the tiles, past the refectory, the chapel, the recreation room and through the main entrance. My progress was, however, halted when I came to the narrow passageway leading down to Sister Clodagh's room. It was in complete darkness. I felt around for a light switch and found nothing but a cold damp wall. Slowly I inched forward, one step at a time. As I rounded a corner, an icy chill suddenly blew through the corridor and almost lifted me off the ground. I stood rooted to the spot. I screamed, which achieved nothing. In fact, I just frightened myself even more. I screamed again. Suddenly a light came on and Sister Clodagh came running around the corner.

"What's wrong? Who is there? Róisín, is that you? … Gráinne what are you doing here? Don't you think you have got into enough trouble for one day? Go to your dorm and get into bed immediately!"

I sprinted out the door, across the courtyard and up the

stairs. The smiling and reassuring face of Matron and a steaming cup of cocoa greeted me as I entered the dorm. I placed the mug on my bedside locker and was in bed slurping the hot cocoa when Sister Clodagh walked in. Matron said goodnight and disappeared into the infirmary. After a few comments about the general untidiness of the dorm, Sister Clodagh turned out the lights and followed.

At about four a.m. I was woken by the sound of somebody crying. At first I thought it was one of the girls in the dorm and ignored it. When it continued, I got out of bed to investigate. All the girls were asleep. Confused, I returned to bed. No sooner had I put my head on the pillow than I heard the girl crying again. I sat up and looked around the room. Everybody was asleep. I slipped out of bed to get a drink of water, but as I reached the sink I saw a light in the courtyard below and a figure standing in the doorway. The crying started again and the figure in the doorway disappeared. I stood silently for about ten minutes, my eyes focused on the doorway.

I returned to my bed and just lay there, staring at the ceiling. I was afraid to close my eyes. I must have because the next thing I remember was been woken the following morning by Sister Clodagh nudging me gently. I looked into her eyes. They were tear-stained. Matron arrived. She always smelled of disinfectant, a stickler for well-made beds, starched shirt collars and well-polished shoes. We walked the short distance down the corridor to the infirmary, which looked out over the front lawns. It was a small intimate room with six beds, three each side, with a huge open fireplace and the obligatory statue of the Blessed Virgin Mary. I imagined in winter it could be very cosy, a thick duck down duvet warmly tucked around my shoulders, a hot water bottle caressing my feet and a coal fire blazing. It would be worth getting a runny nose now and again.

It was now almost seven a.m.. We urgently made our way to the chapel for morning prayers. It was apparent when we reached the main building that there was now an urgency in the school. The nuns glided up and down in their long habits, no apparent sound or movement emanating from their feet. The girls themselves responded by moving with purpose. In short, the school was in gear. Prayers were offered at every opportunity and directed at just about everyone alive and dead, including the poor young souls wandering in the wilderness. "Gone," said Mother Mary, "But never forgotten."

Prayers completed, we engaged in the ritual stampede for breakfast. Over two hundred starving girls with a common mission to reach the refectory in the shortest possible time. Stand in their way at your peril. Even the nuns turned a blind eye to this serious lull in etiquette. I was carried along, my feet hardly touching the ground. Seated at my table, I shamelessly devoured bacon, egg and sausage, a plate of Corn Flakes smothered in thick fresh cream from the school farm. Then I nibbled on delicious warm chunks of crusty bread dripping in creamery butter and strawberry jam. The lay teachers arrived. Maureen made the introductions.

"The little guy with the long greasy hair is Flash. He is nearly fifty and drives a little red MG Midget with no exhaust and two broken spotlights. His girl friend is a middle-aged peroxide blonde called Mandy. He says that she is a model. She may have been, but not this century. He brings her to all the school functions, much to Mother Mary's disgust.

Beside him is Windy. He was to have retired at the end of last year. We even had a party. He has taught in the school for fifty years and has worn the same suit every day.

If you don't believe me, look at the suit he is wearing today and then look the school annual for 1953."

"Why do you call him Windy?" I asked, somewhat naively.

"I will leave that to your imagination!"

"Puff, he's the one with the cigarette ash all over his gown. He is a kindly old devil. Likes his Sweet Afton cigarettes. Can't go twenty minutes without a puff. During class he will open the window, pop up the top of his desk and light up. Whatever about seeing him, you can hear him draw the smoke all the way down to his toes. It's disgusting and he smells awful too."

"Who is the young guy with the glasses?" I enquired.

"That's Brains. He's twenty three, never smiles, always has his head buried in a book. The girls tease him dreadfully. If you talk to him, he fiddles with his tie and goes bright pink. Last year he turned up at the debs in an antiquated dress suit. There were moths and butterflies flying out of his pockets all night."

That left the two elderly ladies at the end of the table. As far as I could see they were dressed all in black. They looked like bit-part actors from a Charles Dickens play. They were, Mo informed me, the Rafter sisters. Nobody knew a great deal about them, not even Sister Clodagh. They were both called Miss Rafter and had been teaching in the school for over sixty years. The only absentee was Foxy, the games master. Normally he would be there, but he went to Galway to play rugby. He would be back tomorrow morning. Over the following months, Foxy was to be singularly responsible for inspiring me to try to emulate Mum's sporting achievements in Mountclare. Against, I must add, my pre-conceived desires and expectations. Foxy was a likeable rogue who would, under no circumstances, accept a negative answer. He was about five foot ten, fortyish, with a head of thinning curly hair which looked like it had been removed from a french poodle's rump. He was extremely fit, if a bit overweight. On Sundays he would bring this little bearded man, Bernard, down to play tennis. Bernard was a bricklayer and lived in Fassaroe in Bray.

Over the following months, we played and worked hard. Indeed, everything moved so fast that Christmas was upon us before we realised it. My achievements were strangely more sporting than academic. I had succeeded in being selected on the Junior hockey and basketball teams and was captain of the first year volleyball team. As Mother Mary declared in my Christmas report,

"While Gráinne's general standard of school work is acceptable, her teachers feel it is by no means a true reflection of her ability. We look forward to a more committed effort from her next term."

Mum and Dad were not at all pleased.

CHAPTER 3

The Christmas holidays were very difficult. I could handle the additional study demanded by Dad, but I could not come to terms with, or understand, what was happening in Mountclare. On four occasions in the weeks leading up to the holidays I was disturbed from my sleep by the same muffled crying and each time I looked out the window, Sister Clodagh stood silhouetted in the courtyard, her lips moving as if in silent prayer, her pearl rosary beads turning and reflecting in the moonlight. One night I woke Eimear and Siobhan and asked them to listen to the woman crying, but they told me that I must be dreaming and to go back to sleep. They could see Sister Clodagh, but heard nothing at all.

We returned to school on January seventh. It was Mum's birthday. Dad treated us to dinner in Ashford. Mum and Dad were very friendly with Paul and Bobby Caprani in Chester Beatty's.

In March, we had to endure the embarrassment of Open Day, the school's annual promotional exercise. In the morning, we had to parade around in gym skirts and short-sleeved blouses performing various forward rolls, handstands, back flips and then finish with an aerobic routine. We were exhausted. The sixth years were excused from performing this year as they had qualified for the finals of the Leinster Senior Hockey Cup. Everybody was looking forward to the match the following Wednesday. In the afternoon, we had to sit through three hours of house awards and rousing speeches. I leaned back in my chair and dozed contentedly in the warm sunlight filtering through the gymnasium windows. Next thing I knew, I was on the flat of my back, my head throbbing and the room echoing with laughter. Before I could get to my feet Matron had taken control, instructing me to remain motionless on the dusty wooden floor.

"Under no circumstances are you to move," Matron demanded.

Mum and Dad's concerned faces appeared above me. Matron continued to check each and every bone in my body and when convinced that nothing was broken, informed me that:

"As you bumped your head, Gráinne, department regulations stipulate that you must remain in the infirmary for observation for a couple of days."

Not a bad idea, I thought smugly.

The stretcher arrived. Matron eased me onto the stretcher and instructed four senior girls to take me directly, and carefully, to the infirmary. She would be along shortly. Mother Mary appeared and beckoned a startled Siobhan to her side.

"Siobhan, after supper you may bring Gráinne's Irish study books to her in the infirmary. This is a great opportunity for her to catch up on her revision. Isn't it Gráinne?"

"An excellent idea, Mother," I agreed.

When we arrived in the infirmary, Sister Clodagh suggested sarcastically that everybody should wait outside while she put the unfortunate patient to bed. Within minutes she had me securely trussed up in bed. Gus and Úna, as she called them, and Doctor Curley arrived and, after satisfying themselves that I would survive, they left.

The dust finally settled. Alone in the infirmary, I headed straight for the television parked neatly in the corner. I switched it on. As always on a Sunday afternoon, there was nothing on. I heard footsteps outside in the hall. I jumped to my feet, ran across the floor and vaulted into bed.

It was Matron. I pretended to be asleep. She tip-toed in, turned off the television and went out, closing the door quietly behind her. I was indeed very comfortable. It was just as I imagined: a blazing coal fire in the corner, a luxurious duck down duvet, scalding radiators throbbing on the walls and a hot water bottle caressing my feet. This would do nicely, I thought, as the wind and rain pounded on the windows and the last of the cars' headlights disappeared down the driveway.

Next morning I was awoken by the other first years washing and dressing. Matron put her head around the door, assured herself that I was still alive and set off down the corridor in pursuit of the stragglers.

Later, Miss Rafter arrived on cue with my Irish test. She sat studying the Irish Times crossword while I struggled with the test.

Tuesday was my third and final day in the infirmary, or so I thought. I was bored, but looking forward to the hockey match the next day. Matron arrived with a cup of tea and two wholegrain biscuits.

"Are you going to the match tomorrow Matron?" I asked excitedly.

"No Gráinne, I have to stay to look after you."

My heart stopped. When I tried to speak, my mouth moved but no words came out. Matron explained.

"You are under observation until six o'clock tomorrow evening. I told you the regulations are that any girl who suffers a head injury must remain in the infirmary for a minimum of seventy-two hours."

I was devastated and tossed and turned all night. When morning finally arrived, I refused to eat my breakfast in silent protest. This was silly as I was hungry. Instead, I lay in bed and listened to the others rising, dressing and breaking into the school war cry as they made their way down to breakfast. An hour later the coaches started to arrive and I watched mournfully as the school excitedly filed out the front door and formed a tunnel. Within minutes the senior team appeared and were clapped and cheered onto the first and most luxurious coach. I looked for Siobhan and Eimear in the crowd. It was not difficult. Siobhan was sitting on Eimear's slender shoulders. Out of the corner of my eye I saw Mother Mary standing at the main door. She too had noticed Siobhan and Eimear. She set off in their direction. I tried banging on the window, which of course was futile. There was no way I could be heard over all this din. As she rounded the last coach, Siobhan turned and saw Mother Mary. She shouted to Eimear to let her down. Eimear did as she was requested, but lost her balance as she leaned forward. The end result was that Siobhan dismounted with all the dignity of a jockey thrown in the Aintree Grand National. They slowly got to their feet and turned to face Mother Mary. There was a deathly silence as Mother Mary regarded the varied expressions of the assembled school and finally the culprits. It was like a scene from the film, "Shoot-Out at the O.K. Corral", that moment when the assorted gang of desperadoes separate. The camera switches from the sheriff - dull, moody and clean shaven, slowly rolling up his shirt sleeve - to the bandit - young, unshaven and chewing defiantly on a mouthful of tobacco. He rolls his tongue and spits. The camera focuses on the vile black liquid in the dust. Their eyes meet.

The silence, as expected, was broken by Mother Mary, but what was not expected was the manner in which she did so. She walked over to Siobhan, dusted her down and laughed. Everyone cheered and returned somewhat bemused to the coaches. Within minutes they were loaded and the large group of excited students and teachers were on their way to Dublin.

Feeling rather sorry for myself, I went back to bed.

CHAPTER 4

Matron woke me at one o'clock for lunch. Observing my sombre appearance, she informed me that when I finished eating I could get dressed. I would be officially discharged from the infirmary at six. Wearily, I dressed and moped around the room. I switched on the television. As usual, there was nothing on. "The Railway Children": steam, smiling faces, steam, rolling countryside, more steam, more smiling faces, boring!, boring! I had read all the magazines. What would the English write about if they hadn't poor Princess Diana and problem pages? I read my own book, which was also about a Princess. "Princess Finola", an evocative book set in ancient Ireland all about Celtic mythology. I had read the book at least five times and each time I read it I enjoyed it more.

Standing by the window, I noticed Matron heading off down the driveway, a bundle of buff envelopes for posting under her arm. She was walking into Rathnew. She would be gone for at least an hour. I decided that I would wander around the deserted school.

I sat for a while in the courtyard looking up at a blue cloudless sky. Despite everything, it was a lovely day. The sun shone. Its rays warmed my back. After a while, dark grey clouds appeared and obscured the sun. It became chilly. Reluctantly, I moved inside. As I passed Sister Clodagh's room, I thought I heard somebody moving around inside. I knocked on the door, gently at first. There was no reply. A little louder. Still no reply. I decided to open the door. Slowly, I turned the old wooden handle and pushed the door open, inch by inch, until I established that the room was empty. I moved further into the room. The door slammed behind me. My heart stopped, my legs went weak, I was rooted to the spot. I turned slowly to face the door. There was nobody there. I sat down on Sister Clodagh's bed.

"Is there anybody there who can help me? Please somebody, anybody, help me."

It was a woman's voice. It sounded like Sister Clodagh, but I couldn't be sure. Where was it was coming from? The woman began to sob.

"Clodagh, are you there? Oh Clodagh, I am so confused. I miss you so much. I need to talk to you? Can you hear me?"

Whoever this woman was, she was certainly calling out to Sister Clodagh. I went over to the door and looked out into the hall. I even walked up as far as the entrance hall. There was nobody. I was alone.

"Who is there? Why don't you talk to me? Can you not hear me either? … Please, oh please talk to me."

The voice echoed all around and appeared to be coming from behind the old door. No it's not possible, I thought. The crying stopped. I looked up and down the passageway and replied anxiously.

"My name is Gráinne."

"Who are you, Gráinne? Can you really hear me? Thank God after twenty years somebody can hear me," the woman declared.

I was struck dumb and could think of nothing to say. My brain was cartwheeling. I must be dreaming. This cannot be happening. Before I had time to reason it all out, the woman spoke again.

"Gráinne, Gráinne, are you still there?"

"Yes, yes I am here," I blurted.

"Who are you? Do you know my sister, Clodagh?"

Intrigued and feeling rather silly, I replied, "Clodagh is gone to the Senior hockey game in Rathfarnham and won't be back until later."

I was terrified, but at the same time fascinated and queried, "You can't be, surely you are not Clodagh's twin sister, Róisín, who went missing twenty years ago? Are you a ghost?"

"I am Róisín and I am certainly not a ghost. I am as alive as you. I have been locked in the past for twenty years. One afternoon during gym, I fell and banged my head. Matron was called and I was sent to the infirmary. I spent the following day in the infirmary while Clodagh went with the Junior hockey team to play in the Leinster Cup in Dublin. Quite by accident, while looking out the infirmary window as the team were leaving, I knocked over a large plaster statue of the Virgin Mary. The head fell off and a very large antique key fell on the floor. I wondered, of course, what the key was doing hidden in the statue and who put it there. I heard Matron on the stairs outside the infirmary, so I hurriedly replaced the head of the statue and put the key in my dressing gown."

"The statue is still there."

Róisín ignored my interruption and continued.

"Later, as it was a lovely day, I decided to go for a walk around the sports fields. I put on my dressing gown and went downstairs. Afterwards, I was thirsty and went through the side door heading for the kitchens. As I passed the door to the secret room, I came across the key in my pocket. The nuns had told us that the door and wall were all that remained of Mountclare Castle, which had been burnt to the ground in 1660. When the nuns bought the estate in 1710, they decided to build the school around the old castle walls. They wished to preserve its memories. Without thinking, I placed the key in the lock and, to my amazement, when I turned the key the mechanism moved and the Door to the Past opened. I went through the door, but forgot to remove the key. As the door closed and locked behind me, Matron came in to the passageway and found the key where I had left it, in the lock. She began praying at the door and called for Fr. Kirkpatrick who, when he arrived, blessed the door. When they were finished, Matron asked him what she should do with the key. He said she had no alternative but to return it to its rightful home, the statue."

"The statue is still there," I repeated. "But why hasn't Clodagh or someone else attempted to let you out?" I asked.

"Gráinne, you must understand. You are the first person I have spoken to from the other side of the door in over twenty years. I can hear Clodagh in her room at night crying and praying. I call out to her, but she does not reply because she cannot hear me. Gráinne, this is no ordinary door. When I came through I travelled back to 1896. That was twenty years ago. Today is Wednesday, April 19th, 1916."

Róisín began to sob once again. I had to at least try and find a way to release her from behind the Door to the Past. But how? That was the problem. The first thing I had to do was to see if the Key to the Past had been returned to the statue. Róisín and I agreed that I should return immediately to the infirmary and find out. With Róisín begging me to hurry, I raced across the courtyard. As I was about to attack the rickety old stairs leading up to the infirmary, Matron appeared at the summit. I was frog marched back to the infirmary and endured the severest of lectures. I sat reading while Matron busied herself in her room. Róisín was surely thinking that I failed to find the Key to the Past and had abandoned her

The team coach arrived back from Dublin at seven p.m.. Matron jumped up out of her chair and rushed down the stairs to greet Mother Mary and the team. Looking out from the infirmary, I saw from the pained expressions alighting from the coaches that Mountclare had obviously not been successful. I could see Matron talking to Mother Mary and then both of them looking up towards the infirmary. There was a knock on the door and, to my relief, Siobhan, and Eimear's smiling faces appeared. They confirmed that we had been beaten. It had been a very rough game. Foxy complained so much that he was cautioned by the referee for using foul and abusive language and, at the end of the game, Mother Mary lodged an official complaint over the quality of refereeing. The supper bell chimed.

As the door closed behind Siobhan and Eimear, I held the statue. My hands were perspiring and my heart thumping. I exerted an upward pressure on the statue's head. At first there was no give. I then twisted it ever so gently to the right and it moved. An extra bit of pressure and the head was in my right hand and the body in my left. I put the head down first and, in doing so, lost my grip on the body and almost dropped what remained of the statue. I went down on my knees to inspect the interior of the statue. I saw what could be a key wrapped in lace. It was an old handkerchief. I knew the minute I started to unfold it that there was a key inside and, judging by the weight and size, it was very old. I heard heavy footsteps on the stairs. It must be Matron with supper. I reunited the head and body of the statue and placed the Key to the Past securely in my pocket. I was standing looking out of the window as Matron entered the infirmary.

I devoured my supper and returned to the dorm. It was a free day, so there was no evening study or prayers. The girls talked excitedly about their day out in Dublin. There was, however, very little spoken about the match. Within the next hour, Sister Clodagh had rounded up the stragglers and turned out the lights. I was nervous that I would fall asleep.

At midnight, I crept out of bed and looked through the window to see if Sister Clodagh was around. Thankfully, she must be asleep. Her light was out. I put on my dressing gown and slippers, sneaked down the stairs and across the cobblestones to the side entrance. Sister Clodagh's door was closed. I could hear her radio playing. I turned towards the old door opposite, removed the key from my pocket, unwrapped the old lace handkerchief and inserted the key into the lock. I could feel the mechanism responding.

CHAPTER 5

The lock clicked once … twice …, I turned the handle and leaned against the Door to the Past. It didn't give. I looked up and down the corridor, gripped the key firmly and turned it again in the same direction. Still the door remained locked. Perspiration was now running freely down my face, neck and back. The cold air filtering down the corridor chilled my bones. I shivered involuntarily. I turned the key and pulled the door towards me. The door opened! I removed the key and placed it back in the pocket of my dressing gown. The old door creaked loudly as I opened it inwards. Cautiously, I eased myself around the half-opened door. Behind me I heard Sister Clodagh's door open. I moved further into the darkness, turned and closed over the Door to the Past.

I stood stock still in the eerie darkness. My heart was pounding, I was freezing, my night dress, wet from nervous perspiration, stuck uncomfortably to my back. After a few minutes, I regained some of my composure and noticed a light flickering in the distance.

I failed to realise that I was standing on the top of a staircase and, as a result, went tumbling head over heels through the darkness, finally coming to a halt on a rough wooden floor. I passed out.

I was woken by somebody splashing cold water on my face. Through the mist and pain in my head, I recognised the face of the woman bent over me.

"Where am I? Sister Clodagh what are you doing here? Where am I?. Is it time to get up yet? I had a dream!"

"I'm not Sister Clodagh. I'm Róisín, her twin. You must be Gráinne. You have travelled back in time."

A nun, almost six feet tall, appeared from behind

Róisín's shoulder. Róisín jumped to attention.

"Sister Mary Francis, I ..."

"Róisín! What on earth are you doing here? Where did this vagrant come from? What is she doing here in the scullery in her night clothes? I sincerely hope that none of the kitchen staff have been harbouring this child. Call the head gardener, Mr Clarke, and have her taken to the police station in Wicklow. On second thought, I had better deal with this myself. Will you never learn? Do you not remember the trouble these children caused last summer? Come child, follow me!"

Róisín leaned over and whispered, "To survive, you must appear normal. Speak only when you are spoken to. Remember that you speak a modern language. People of today will not understand you."

I picked myself up, mindful that what I had done was reckless and that my disappearance would undoubtedly cause considerable distress, but I was eager to explore this new world. I obediently followed the nun out of the scullery and into the early morning sunlight. I was filthy dirty and it was little wonder Sister Mary Francis thought I was a vagrant.

It was strange walking across the courtyard. The cobblestones were brighter, the stairs much firmer and the cut stone of the coach house was exposed. Matron was a portly woman who, surprisingly, lived in Rathnew and wasn't a nun. Sister Mary Francis retreated and Matron ushered me into a communal bathroom and proceeded to fill a huge bath with lukewarm water that had been simmering on the old wood stove in the corner. She told me to strip and get into the bath. She then set about removing every piece of flesh from my body and every hair in my head with a scrubbing brush and this foul-smelling red carbolic soap. It was degrading, yet invigorating.

Matron instructed me to dry myself. While I was doing that, she would locate some clothes for me in the laundry.

I remembered the Key to the Past and rummaged through my nightdress. To my relief it was still in my pocket, wrapped in the lace handkerchief. I quickly hid it in a water urn.

Matron returned, placing a variety of clothes on the sideboard. I did not know where to start. It was a warm spring day and Matron had left calf-length laced walking boots, complete with steel heel and toe caps, hairy knee length woollen socks, a red ankle-length skirted petticoat, double frill knickers, high-necked white cotton shirt with a starched collar, a navy quilted skirt trimmed with blue bands, a black woollen shawl and a linen head covering.

In a convent, mirrors were thought to inspire vanity, a sin, so I had no opportunity to inspect my reflection. I retrieved the Key to the Past from the urn and placed it safely in my pocket. After a few minutes Matron re-appeared and led me back to where Sister Mary Francis had first deposited me.

"What's wrong, girl?" Mr Clarke asked angrily as we walked across the courtyard.

"Why are you crying? All the Constabulary will do is send you to the orphanage in Rathdrum. Think yourself lucky. It's a hell of a lot better than walking the streets barefoot and hungry."

A young boy appeared, leading a bay Connemara pony pulling a small two-seater trap. Mr Clarke took the reins and motioned for me to climb in.

We headed off down the driveway, the pony fighting desperately to move through the deep gravel. Moving away from the school and heading out into the country, the landscape appeared sharper and devoid of industrial mist.

"What do you think of my sign?" asked Mr Clarke

proudly as we drove out through the entrance gates.

"I made it last week," he boasted.

"I bet it will last for years," I replied.

CHAPTER 6

It was a lovely day and, despite my fears, I relaxed and soaked up the atmosphere. The road from Mountclare to Rathnew was really nothing more than a narrow dirt track and the trap swung from side to side as it wedged in the deep ridges made by larger forms of transport. There was great excitement in Rathnew caused by the number of uniformed soldiers marching up and down the street. Mr Clarke told me that the British army often came down from Dublin on manoeuvres and camped on the Murrough.

"Do you know the De la Salle school on the Murrough?" he enquired. "Well, up to recently it used to be the Militia headquarters. The Army sold it to the brothers, but they still use the grounds to camp. Many of the officers' and soldiers' families continue to live in or around Rathnew."

The road to Wicklow was in terrible condition. It was dusty due to the dry weather and, like the back road to Rathnew, full of pot holes and ridges which made the journey most uncomfortable.

When we arrived in Wicklow town, there was a crowd gathering on the footpaths around Fitzwilliam Square. A constable stepped out and instructed Mr Clarke to pull in immediately as the Assize was due from Rathdrum.

"What is the Assize?" I enquired of Mr Clarke.

Suddenly, the street echoed to the sound of galloping hooves. I turned and saw a regiment of mounted police in splendid blue uniforms. They sat proudly astride magnificent dark bay horses, whose nostrils flared and tails swished as they thundered up Abbey Street. They were escorting a highly ornate black coach pulled by two equally proud grey horses. Taking up the rear were two further mounted police. When the excitement died down, Mr Clarke calmly picked up the reins and explained that the Assize was the district judge. We continued on to the police station.

The duty sergeant was seated behind a loose wooden partition reading a well-thumbed copy of the Irish Times. Mr Clarke relayed his message.

"Sister Mary Francis in Mountclare told me to deliver this vagrant. We found her wandering around the school this morning in her night clothes. As far as we know, she has not stolen anything."

The burly, red-haired sergeant rose slowly and walked over to the opening, crudely cut into the partition. He obviously suffered from a bad back as he used the corner of the table he was seated at to ease himself up.

"Right, my girl," he said. "You had better follow me. It appears you have some explaining to do. Should you choose not to co-operate, you will be brought before the Courts. Mr Clarke, you may leave now. I will contact the school as soon as I have any information about this young lady."

The sergeant led me down a dark corridor and into what I took to be an interrogation room. He lit a gas wall lamp. The smell reminded me of my uncle's caravan. There was a small pine kitchen table in the centre of the room surrounded by four similarly styled kitchen chairs. He motioned for me to sit on one of the chairs while he sat on the corner of the table. He stared at me for a few moments, then leaned forward to adjust the turn-ups on his heavy twill trousers. The table started to sway and he lost his balance as one of the legs buckled and collapsed under his weight. He ended up face down on the floor. Even in these hostile conditions, I managed to smile.

He looked up at me from the floor, put his hand in the

small of his back, winced, raised himself to his elbows and twisted his ridiculous handlebar moustache between his forefinger and thumb … and laughed.

"Come on, girl. Give me a hand up," he said.

Once he regained his composure, he righted the table, kicked the leg back into position and sat opposite. This time he sat on one of the sturdy chairs.

"Open out your pockets and let me see if you have removed anything from the school."

I began to panic. I had the Key to the Past in the pocket of my skirt. I fumbled around and mumbled that I didn't have anything belonging to the school. He looked directly at me, his eyes narrowing, and demanded that I reveal the linings of my pockets immediately.

"All of them," he repeated, pointing directly to the pocket containing the key. Slowly I removed the lace handkerchief trying, unsuccessfully, to conceal the Key to the Past inside. He reached out and took the handkerchief in his hand and shook it. The key fell heavily onto the table.

"What are you doing with this key? It has the school crest stamped on the underside. I will telephone Sister Mary Francis. You remain here," he said.

He locked the door behind him and was gone for almost an hour when the gas flame started to flicker. Suddenly, the globe exploded and I was alone in the dark. Frightened, I jumped to my feet and made for the door. I listened at the locked door. All I could hear was the sound of the gas escaping from the light fitting. I was now becoming light-headed and my eyes were beginning to sting. I started to shout and bang frantically on the door. The gas started to burn my lungs. I was losing consciousness.

The next thing I remember was lying awkwardly on the narrow steps of the police station. Róisín was stroking my head. I heard the sergeant behind me say, "She will be alright now. The silly girl tried to take her life."

Róisín saw me coming round and smiled as she helped me to my feet. I did not feel at all well and sat down. The sergeant handed me back the lace handkerchief, without the key.

"Miss Gráinne, there is something decidedly odd about you and I am damned if I know what it is. Since you arrived this morning, you have reacted to the hostility of the station and my enquiries with the presence of an educated and liberated woman of double your years. You have not spoken a single word in anger or despair. It is my opinion that you are not a vagrant, but something beyond my present understanding and at this time I will choose, despite my better judgement, to bow to Sister Mary Francis's wishes and strike what happened today from the records."

With that, he turned and disappeared into the station. I was helped down the stone steps by Róisín and Mr Clarke and into a much larger trap. I was feeling very weak and my eyes were streaming. Nevertheless, I relaxed in the softly sprung bench seat in the back of the buggy.

"Mr Clarke, please drop the hood of the trap. It's a lovely day. Miss Gráinne needs all the fresh air she can get. Then you may take us directly to Gilletley's jewellers."

Mr Clarke grunted as he let down the hood. As he tied it in place, the sergeant appeared running down the steps. When he reached the trap, he handed Mr Clarke the Key to the Past and told him that he had just spoken to Sister Mary Francis on the phone and she said that he was to take great care of the key and take it directly to her on his return.

I had forgotten the Key to the Past. How could I do such a thing? Without the Key, Róisín and I were locked in the past.

Róisín instructed Mr Clarke to proceed to Gilletley's.

When we got there, she climbed down from the trap and instructed me to remain where I was. Mr Clarke was instructed to turn the trap around as she wanted to bring me down to the quay side. As we sat in silence awaiting Róisín's return, I had my first opportunity to observe Wicklow town. There was a whole array of smells, the most dominant being burning turf and fish. On every corner there were women selling herrings from old wicker baskets. The street was covered in horse and cattle manure. Every time a carriage or trap passed, a huge cloud of dust was raised from a road surface that was made up of grit and loose gravel. Mr Clark took a grubby handkerchief from his pocket and, as he wiped grit from his eyes, turned to an elderly man standing in Gilletley's doorway and enquired, "Where is the watering cart today?"

"The Royal Mail commandeered Mr Hagan's horse to pull the Mail Van. Their horse is lame," the old man replied.

"What is a watering car?" I asked Róisín when she came out of the jewellers. She ignored my question and instead handed me a neatly wrapped parcel. Then she said, "It is a cart filled with a large tank of water and is used in dry weather to damp down the dust on the streets."

I opened the parcel slowly and, to my surprise and delight, it was a beautiful gold pocket watch. It was called a traveller's watch. I was delighted with my present and thanked Róisín, who replied with tears in her eyes, "It's just nice to have someone to buy a present for ... I have waited twenty years for this moment."

Róisín regained her composure and informed us that she would return presently. I settled back to inspect my watch. Across the road was The Green Tree Hotel, beside it Carr's Tea Rooms, further up beyond the square I could make out the names of another two tea rooms and a hardware shop. This wasn't like a normal hardware shop.

They sold everything: women's and children's clothes, fruit, wheel barrows, vegetables and medicines. Róisín returned and instructed Mr Clarke to drive us down to South Quay and then back to the Green Tree Hotel.

"In order that we could partake of afternoon tea," she said.

It was now two-thirty. As we made our way down to the quay, I noted that there were no cars on the streets, only horses and donkeys pulling a wide variety of carts, traps and carriages and those big black bicycles. The only motorised vehicle in evidence that day was an enormous tractor parked outside the Wicklow Hotel in Market Square. Róisín told me that it was the first in Wicklow and it was called the Whiting Bull. It was a few years old now, but it still caused quite a stir when it arrived in the town.

I was delighted Róisín suggested going down to the quays. In 1916, they were the commercial heart of the town and lined in enormous, random piles of wood and coal. Róisín explained that the wood came from the Coolatin estate in Shillelagh and was on its way to Wales to be used as props in mine shafts. Coal was dispatched to Wicklow by return. The sea, in the early part of the century, she continued, was the only link between trading countries and it was only through the introduction of air travel in the latter part of the century that it was considered a barrier, rather than a link. While the main street was inactive, the quays, in total contrast, were bursting with life. Men and boys of every age, colour and class ran to and fro calling out in a wide variety of languages. We dismounted from the buggy and walked a while. There were boats of every kind tied up to the quay. In fact, it was almost impossible to walk more than five paces without coming across a tie rope. The wooden tall ships were magnificent. These majestic vessels dwarfed all other boats. I could not help but wonder that, while they appeared romantic, the crews' soiled appearance implied that life on board was anything but comfortable. We stood a while, silently soaking up the atmosphere. Mr Clarke interjected and informed us that it would be dark soon and, if we still intended to partake of afternoon tea, we should hasten to the Green Tree. We climbed back into the trap and headed for the Murrough. On our way we passed another tall ship, this time being loaded with copper and lead from the mines in Avoca. We crossed Bachelor's Bridge and admired the old Militia building now inhabited by the De La Salle brothers. Camped in the grounds were close to one hundred white bell tents of varying sizes belonging to the Cheshire regiment we had seen in Rathnew. Róisín told me that last November there was a terrible storm of hurricane proportions that battered the east coast for almost twenty-four hours and that a large Greek coal boat ran aground, scattering its cargo on the Murrough.

The main street was deserted when we arrived at the Green Tree Hotel. Standing at the front door remonstrating with the porter were five bedraggled street urchins. These were itinerant children, Róisín explained, about nine or ten years old. They had been abandoned by their families and refused to live in the orphanages. They survived by stealing and begging. I regarded them for a few moments, then sadly realised that not alone were they barefoot, but it was impossible to tell whether or not they were boys or girls. They were boys. All had their heads shaven. One wore what was once a splendid red velvet dress over which, on his narrow shoulders, hung a buttonless British military army jacket. The sleeves were too long for his short arms, so the cuffs had been crudely hacked off by some blunt instrument. Another had a piece of old sack cloth tied around his waist in the shape of a skirt. It was supported by a piece of frayed rope. Over this he wore a pink frilled ladies' blouse and a grey mutton sleeved jacket. They were indeed a bizarre sad troop adorned in this strange array of male and female clothes, each with abnormally large and deformed feet.

Afternoon tea in the Green Tree was a delightful experience. We left Mr Clarke in the shade of the big tree. The hotel was very busy. There were uniformed waitresses running around in all directions, trays laden with neatly cut sandwiches and delicious cream cakes. A young waitress arrived with the cream tea closely followed by another with two silver trays, one with a selection of sandwiches, the other cream cakes. I was famished and set about devouring the delicious cream cakes while Róisín continued her story.

After she came through the door, she made her way in the dark to the kitchens. She was not aware that she had travelled back in time. When confronted by members of the kitchen staff, she appeared quite mad. and was duly dispatched by train that night to Dr Steevens's hospital in Dublin. Dr Kilvary, a junior doctor from Ballina, was on duty that night and befriended Róisín. It was this friendship that saved Róisín from being sent to an orphanage. Instead, a friend of the doctor's, Constance, on Dr Kilvary's prompting, offered Róisín employment as a groom on her family estate, Lissadell, eight miles north of Sligo. Dr Kilvary met Constance Gore-Booth when her younger sister, Eva, was referred to him, suffering from what was then a deadly disease, consumption. Constance was twenty-eight years old and still lived at home with her family, but hoped to travel to Paris to study art early the following year. She needed a groom to look after her horses while she was abroad. Róisín was informed in no uncertain terms that Lissadell would be preferable to an orphanage and arrived within the week on the Sligo train full of hope and enthusiasm.

According to Róisín, Lissadell was a fine estate. Indeed, the driveway leading to the forty-eight room, two-storey-over-basement mansion was almost two and a half miles long, running through a forest and along by the sea. It was a vibrant and exciting place to be. Róisín was accepted into the extended family and luckily, like politics, her past was never discussed. At first she lived about half a mile from the main house with the farm manager and his wife in a two-storey stone cottage in sight of the very extensive stable yard. Soon after, Róisín moved into the main house. Her bedroom, one of twelve, was over the entrance portico. Constance had two younger brothers and sisters and that summer they gathered in the family home. Even though they were all in their twenties and quite a bit older than Róisín, they included her in all the many and varied activities: picnics on the beach, riding, cricket and croquet on the lawn. Constance loved to fish and spent hours on her own, sailing in the bay in front of the house. Róisín adored Constance, but could not understand why she fought and argued so much with her family, especially her father Henry, whom Róisín found to be particularly charming. The estate tenants and workers endorsed Róisín's feelings. They had nothing but the highest regard for the Gore-Booths, past and present. The Anglo-Irish landlords were not generally known for their compassion towards their dependants. But during the more difficult times, it was recorded that the Gore-Booths took food from their own tables and distributed it by hand to their tenants. They also reduced rents and allowed those in distress to dig turf, free of charge. As a result, the Gore-Booths had to sell and re-mortgage their land to support their tenants. Constance's eldest brother, Josslyn, followed in his father's footsteps and actually worked with Sir Horace Plunkett in setting up The Irish Agricultural Organisation, which worked to establish co-operatives for the tenant farmers.

There was always a vast and wonderful array of people staying at the big house and at night time they entertained themselves with piano and organ recitals or acted out plays in front of the large marble fireplace in the gallery room. Many of these plays actually went on to be performed in Sligo, the proceeds donated to a local charity. Constance was an excellent actress and loved to be the centre of attention. Winter arrived all too soon and with it brought Constance's favourite pastimes - hunting and shooting. As a fourteen year old, Constance rode to hounds with the Sligo Hunt, famed in Ireland for their fearsome, if foolhardy, approach to hunting.

Christmas saw Eva return from Italy. She had been sent to a warmer, less damp climate for health reasons. Eva informed Constance and Mabel, their youngest sister, about the suffrage movement that had been set up in England. Their aim was to fight for women's rights, including the right to vote. The three sisters formed a committee. Constance was elected president and the movement was launched at a large public meeting held in the local schoolhouse. Constance was, however, uneasy in Sligo. She wanted to go to art college in Paris. This was the reason Róisín had initially travelled to Lissadell, to look after Constance's horses while she studied in Paris. Her parents were not keen, but finally relented in February. When the hunting season ended, Constance set off for Paris via London. Róisín missed Constance dreadfully and soon became unhappy in Lissadell. She decided to leave and wrote to Constance in May explaining that she desired to return to her family in Wicklow. On June 15th, Róisín arrived back at Mountclare with excellent references from the Gore-Booths and applied for a job in the kitchens.

Mr Clarke appeared at the french doors.

"It's close to four o'clock, miss. They are lighting the street lights. We should make our way back to the school."

Róisín told him that we would be out in a few minutes and to return and watch over the trap.

"What is to happen to me in Mountclare?" I enquired.

"I told Sister Mary Francis that you were a cousin of the Gore-Booths and were staying with Constance in Dublin. When Constance heard that you were visiting Ashford, she suggested that you call on me in Rathnew. I told her that you got confused and took directions for Rathdrum and not Rathnew, thus arriving in Mountclare after nightfall. I said that I found you in a distressed state and put you straight to bed. You awoke early and, while looking for the washroom, lost your footing on the stairs and fell heavily where I found you. I informed her that Friday morning next we had planned to travel to Dublin to stay with the Countess for Easter."

"Who is the Countess?" I enquired.

Róisín stood up, handed the uniformed head waitress three large copper coloured coins and replied, "We really must go now. Believe me, there isn't time to explain."

As we reached the front door, however, she whispered, "Sixteen years ago, Constance married Casimir, a Polish Count she met in the art school in Paris. She is now known publicly as the Countess Markievicz, but her friends call her Madame."

FRIDAY APRIL 21ST

Friday morning at six a.m., while the school slept peacefully, Róisín and I breakfasted on sweet milky tea, brown bread and porridge. Sister Mary Francis left Mountclare at dawn on Thursday morning to go on retreat. There was no alternative. I had to travel to Dublin with Róisín. I was uneasy and had the distinct impression that I may not be welcome in the Countess's house. At seven-thirty a.m. we set off to catch the eight-twenty train to Dublin. The trip to the station outside Wicklow town took about twenty minutes. It was almost eight o'clock and there was still a long queue spilling out of the ticket office and half way down the approach road. Men, women and children struggled with luggage up the steady incline to the station.

There was great excitement on the platform as the steam locomotive's arrival was heralded by its distinctive whistle. "The Stillorgan" was the name painted in gold lettering with blue shading. It appeared from a siding on the Murrough and came to a grinding halt, clouds of steam billowing in every direction. The eight-twenty to Dublin had arrived five minutes late. It was truly a magnificent spectacle - the grinding and scraping of the big wheels as they fought for traction, the damp smell of the steam and the black soot that fell from the copper topped chimneys, soiling everything it came in contact with. Steam engines were romantic, but dirty. Behind the train was the tender, which carried the coal to stoke the fire. Behind that again were five carriages: one first class, one second class and two third class. Linking the first and second class carriages was the fifth, a catering carriage. We travelled second class. The carriage had five small individual compartments and a toilet. It was acceptable, if a little cramped. Our small compartment seated ten on two well-sprung bench seats upholstered in a green flowered tapestry. The first class carriage was the same overall size but had a much higher standard of trim. The panelling was in mahogany and sycamore and the upholstery a plush green velvet. First class had only four compartments, two toilets, gas reading lights and a dog box built into the outside of the carriage. Róisín liked to travel first class on long journeys, but the return fare to Harcourt Street first class cost three shillings. Second class was only two shillings. It really wasn't worth paying another shilling for a short sixty-five minute train journey. I didn't get a chance to see the conditions of the third class carriages but Róisín told me that when the school sent her to Steevens's hospital she had to travel third class and she was terrified. There was a group of drunken soldiers who fought all the way to Bray. One of them actually urinated on the floor while another smashed a window with his rifle. Róisín said she cowered in a corner while women screamed, children cried and dogs growled. There were just rows of wooden bench seats, some of which the soldiers duly demolished and threw out the window. When they reached Bray, the soldiers were arrested by the Constabulary.

We arrived in Dublin around a quarter to ten. Madame's house in Leinster Road was only a short walk from Harcourt Street Station. We ran down the stone steps and out into Harcourt Street.

Róisín spoke at length on the train, preparing me for the contrasts between the rich and poor living in Dublin. It had occurred to me as the train pulled out of Wicklow that Róisín had become more intense and easily agitated. She spoke aggressively about the poor and how they were dependant on the unwanted possessions of the rich. She had even seen children in winter searching in dustbins outside the big houses in Rathmines for half-burnt cinders, which they carried away in tin cans As we reached street level, I was almost knocked to the ground by a troop of about twenty barefooted vagrant boys similar to those I had witnessed in Wicklow. Broom handles and various lengths of wood rested on their thin shoulders. They stopped in front of Róisín, saluted, and marched on in military formation towards Stephen's Green. Róisín drew to attention and saluted back. When they were out of sight, Róisín picked up her suitcase and took me by the arm. In silence, we turned left and walked up to the corner of Harcourt Road. We turned right and crossed over the road and headed up towards Harrington Street. We had to stop before crossing at the very busy intersection linking Charlotte Street and Charlemont Street. As we waited to cross the road, a giant police constable directed the traffic. He was well over six feet tall, with his spiked helmet, he looked almost seven. Róisín explained later that he was a member of the Dublin Metropolitan Police. A condition of acceptance into the force was that all members must be over six feet two inches tall.

While we waited for a break in the traffic, I had an excellent opportunity to absorb the sights and sounds of Dublin at the turn of the century. I now understood what Róisín meant by the people of Dublin living in a barefoot and bowler society. Everywhere I looked well-dressed opulent men in bowler hats and dark suits strolled with elegantly-dressed ladies in summer suits. Beside us waiting to cross was a stunning young woman in a navy blue silk suit with a white lace collar and a black satin sash. Her skirt was full and embroidered in the most delicate of laces I had ever seen. She was escorted by a distinguished elderly gentleman in a bowler hat. He wore a navy single-breasted morning coat over a double-breasted matching waistcoat with yellow spots. His trousers were also navy with a thin stripe. Both wore black laced boots. She was also accompanied by a nurse pushing a big black pram and a nanny who securely held the chubby hands of two small children. Behind them, leaning against a hoarding advertising Cantrell & Cochrane's Club Soda and "Dicksalata Absolutely Waterproof Boots", were two barefoot young girls.

The trams made a tremendous racket as they rattled along, crossing and recrossing the tracks buried in the cobblestones. The emergency fenders on the front swept away any thing or body that got in its way. They scraped the ground as the tram dipped into pot holes. At night time, they were spectacular as they travelled in a halo of yellow light, sparks flashing from the trolley heads above. A Guinness dray, pulled by a hairy-footed Clydesdale and laden with wooden casks, passed. As it did so, Róisín and I ran across the road and into O'Conner's bakery. The owner, Mrs O'Conner-Cox, who was responsible for the vast array of glorious smells, was arranging cakes under a glass counter. When she saw Róisín, she wiped her hands in a teacloth, ran around the counter and smothered Róisín in hugs and kisses. Delia, as she was called, was a wonderful character and happily engaged her customers in idle chat. More importantly she was a kind woman, too. Not long after we arrived, a young blind woman who had fallen on hard times struggled into the shop. On her back, looking over her shoulder, was a young child, secured only by a dirty woollen blanket tied in a knot around her painfully slim waist. She came to the counter and asked courteously for a loaf of stale bread. Delia obliged, but placed a fresh loaf in the woman's bag. The woman opened her purse allowing Delia to extract payment. Delia rummaged with her right hand in the blind woman's purse and, instead of taking money out of the purse, she actually deposited a sixpence she had in her left hand. It was a very moving experience. Here was one person giving charity to another without looking for any form of recognition whatsoever.

"Gráinne, excuse my manners. Why don't you go upstairs? There is a pot of tea on the range and fresh cakes on the dresser."

Upstairs, I poured myself a cup of tea and selected a fresh cream slice made from the most delicate of pastry. I walked over to a window facing out over Harcourt Road. I noticed on an easy chair beside the window a letter from the Irish Citizen Army. It was dated Wednesday, April 19th, 1916. It was addressed to: "Those Dedicated to the Independence of Ireland" and was signed Constance Markievicz. Folded neatly next to it was a newspaper, "The Workers' Republic". Inside the newspaper was a large single sheet of folded paper. I opened it ...

Poblacht Na hÉireann
The Provisional Government
of the
Irish Republic
to the People of Ireland

Irishmen and Irishwomen: In the name of God and of the dead generations from which she receives her old tradition of nationhood, Ireland through us, summons her children to her flag and strikes for her freedom ...

There was a noise on the stairs. I quickly folded the proclamation and put it back in the newspaper. Delia came into the room, picked up the letter and the proclamation, and disappeared back down the stairs into the shop. I began to read the "Workers' Republic". It was the April 22nd edition. I thumbed through it quickly. It was very political. A poem was ringed in pencil, it concluded:

> *So we're waiting till 'Somebody' gives the word*
> *That sends us to freedom or death;*
> *As free men defiant we'd sooner fall*
> *Than be slaves to our dying breath.*

It was signed "Constance Markievicz Irish Citizen Army" and was dedicated to all the national women's organisations advancing the cause of Irish liberty.

As I walked into the shop, I found Róisín and Delia behind the counter discreetly studying the proclamation. Delia, smiling, declared, "The time has finally come, Róisín. It's hard to believe that all those long hours, planning and field training are about to be put to the ultimate test."

Róisín saluted Delia, picked up her suitcase and disappeared up Harcourt Road. I thanked Delia for her hospitality and ran out into the street looking for Róisín. I found her heading towards South Richmond Street. When I caught up with her, I asked her to explain what Delia meant by the ultimate test. Deep in thought, Róisín was agitated by my untimely intrusion.

"In order that you may understand what is meant by the ultimate test, I must bring you up to date with the Countess Markievicz story. When Madame went to art school in Paris, she met and fell in love with another aspiring artist, the Count Markievicz. He was a tall, handsome, athletic man, six years her junior. Casimir, or Cassie as he was known, lost his wife in childbirth twelve months previously. He was a champion cyclist and fencer. They married in London in September 1900 and then returned to Paris to live. They left Paris the following summer as Madame, then pregnant, insisted that the baby be born in the family home in Sligo. Maeve was born that November. Three months later, Madame and Cassie returned once again to Paris, leaving Maeve with her Grandmother in Sligo.

The following spring they decided to return to Dublin, so along with Stasko, Cassie's four year old son by his first wife, and Maeve, now almost two, they set up home in "St Mary's", Frankfort Avenue, Rathgar. Over the following four years, Madame and Cassie immersed themselves in all the Anglo-Irish, social and artistic movements. Indeed, they were instrumental in setting up the United Arts Club in Fitzwilliam Square in Dublin. Madame was almost forty and a noted socialite, but she began to tire of the seemingly endless merry-go-round of balls and parties and grew increasingly unhappy with the poverty witnessed on the streets of Dublin and more so with the continued occupation and attitude of the British in Ireland. That summer Madame rented a small white-washed cottage set in the Dublin mountains."

As we approached Portobello bridge, a shrill blast from a siren interrupted Róisín. I jumped up on the wall just in time to see a Guinness barge with its black funnel lowered disappear under the bridge. I ran across the bridge, narrowly missing a butcher's delivery bicycle, and just caught the long boat, its rows of neatly stacked barrels appearing out of the arch on the other side. The crew were dressed in navy with peaked caps, the word Guinness printed in red letters across their large muscular chests. I stood transfixed as the barge spluttered and chugged into the distance. I rejoined Róisín, who had been waiting patiently, and we crossed over the road and headed up Lower Rathmines Road. Róisín continued:

"The previous tenant of the cottage left numerous

nationalist newspapers behind him, the common theme being that only in a free Ireland governed by Irish people could the Irish gain prosperity and regain pride in their rich culture. She read with interest about Sinn Fein's struggle for independence and of past attempts by men such as Hugh O'Neill, Wolfe Tone and Robert Emmet.

Madame returned to Dublin and attempted to join Sinn Fein, which means "ourselves". Arthur Griffith, who formed Sinn Fein, ignored her request to join. He could not accept that a woman of Madame's background was anything other than a British spy. Madame persevered and the following year became a member of the Drumcondra branch through a friendship she developed with a young man called Bulmer Hobson who is Vice President of Sinn Fein. Madame then joined Inghinidhe na hÉireann (Daughters of Ireland) set up by Maud Gonne. Their objectives were similar to Sinn Fein's, that is to promote independence from England among Irish women. Madame was duly elected to a committee set up to produce a newspaper called "Bean na hÉireann" (Women of Ireland). Two years later, Madame was informed that the Viceroy, the British Monarch's representative in Ireland, was about to form a troop of boy scouts in Dublin. Incensed that this group of young men would salute a flag that flew in triumph over every defeat this nation had ever known, she immediately formed a rival troop consisting of eight young students from Brunswick Street National School. They were originally named after an ancient Irish band of warriors called the Red Branch Knights. This name was changed to The Fianna, another ancient band of elite warriors. Their ranks swelled to over one hundred as the result of an advertisement that appeared in a newspaper looking for boys "willing to work for the Independence of Ireland."

We walked up Rathmines Road, past the Y.M.C.A. and to Rathmines Church. Róisín saw me straining to look at the enormous green dome reflecting the sunlight on the roof of the church. She told me it was inspired by St Peter's Basilica in Rome, then continued:

"Madame was deeply moved by the misery and hunger the children living on the streets and in tenements were subjected to. She established, with Maud Gonne, children's food kitchens in two city centre national schools. They served over two hundred and fifty meals per day. While Madame was caring for the children living in the many tenements in Dublin, a man called Jim Larkin was establishing the I.T.G.W.U. (The Irish Transport and General Workers Union). The aim of the union was to protect the interests of their members by demanding that employers improve wages and working conditions. Madame remarked to me once, 'Larkin forced his self reliance and respect on his members and, from that day, I looked upon him as a friend and would do any thing to help him.'.

"She didn't realise it at the time, but she would get this opportunity sooner than she thought. The employers formed their own association, the D.E.F. (Dublin Employers' Federation), to oppose Larkin's I.T.G.W.U.. They refused to employ any of their members. Soon close to 25,000 people were out of work in what was called The Lock Out. The aim of the employers was to starve the workers into submission. Larkin counteracted by contacting sympathetic trade unions all over England. He requested food and money. Madame set up a food kitchen in union headquarters at Liberty Hall. Constant unprovoked attacks by the Constabulary on union members forced Larkin to set up an armed force called the Irish Citizen Army. Madame initially held the position of treasurer on the army council. Despite the hardship endured, by the end of February The

Lock Out was over. The workers, beaten into submission, relented and returned to work. Nobody won. The employers had lost money and production and were now aware of the growing strength and determination of the Union.

We had reached Rathmines Town Hall and had just crossed over at the public library when the sound of galloping hooves and clanging bells came from behind. I looked around. Racing towards us was a red fire engine pulled by two heavily muscled grey horses. All road traffic pulled into the footpaths while pedestrians turned to review this remarkable spectacle. As the fire engine passed, one could not but admire this fine band of men. Some were seated, others standing, but all were proud and erect with their highly polished brass helmets and knee length leather boots. The fire engine turned up Castlewood Avenue. I glanced at the Town Hall clock. It was eleven-thirty. On the wall under the clock was a poster advertising:

The Rathmines and Rathgar Musical Society perform
Gilbert & Sullivan's popular opera The Mikado.
Monday April 17th, Town Hall Rathmines.
Six nights at 8 p.m. & Matinee Saturday at 2.30 p.m.

"The house is not far from here," said Róisín as we walked up Leinster Road. It's number 49B, almost on the corner of Grosvenor Square."

"Go on. Finish the story," I pleaded.

"The I.T.G.W.U. presented Madame with an honorary membership and a decorated manuscript in recognition of her unselfish and earnest labours during The Lock Out. Unfortunately, as a result of her extensive physical and financial contributions to the Union, Sinn Fein, Irish Citizen Army, the Fianna and the many National Women's Associations, Cassie left Madame and returned with Stasko to the Ukraine. He joined the Imperial Hussar Cavalry. Maeve returned to live with her grandmother in Sligo. Madame paid the highest price in her quest for Irish Independence.

"There is a determination within the movements that believe that the only way to return Ireland to the Irish is through an armed struggle - the ultimate test Delia spoke of. We have been preparing now for over eighteen months since war was declared in Europe. Next Sunday, April 23rd we are to move on the General Post Office in O'Connell street and proclaim the Provisional Government of the Irish Republic. We must strike now while England is at war in Europe. In peacetime, they would be free to crush us."

We arrived at "Surrey House". It was not at all what I expected. I imagined a much grander house, Georgian, double fronted, with neat lawns rolling into the distance, a gravelled driveway winding around the tennis court, and swimming pool, gardeners and uniformed staff running around pruning and serving iced drinks to the guests on the croquet lawn, beautiful women reclining on sun loungers, protected from prying eyes by a formidable stone wall and an endless variety of ornamental shrubs and trees. Madame would greet us formally on the granite steps and detail the butler to remove our cases to our suite reserved in the west wing. Instead, I found number 49B to be a narrow, three-storey, brick-built semi-detached house with a tiny front garden. Six uniformed young men, no more than fifteen-years-old were playing cards, some kneeling, others sitting on orange boxes.

"They are members of the Fianna," said Róisín.

Two enormous Dublin Metropolitan Policemen were leaning against the wall on the opposite side of the road making notes. The hall door opened. Standing there was a badly dressed woman in an old tweed jacket with no buttons, just a safety pin pulling it roughly together. If she was wearing a blouse, I could not see it. Her skirt, which was also tweed but of a poorer quality, had been darned badly and fell unevenly around her calves. She wore odd wool stockings. The elastic had snapped on one stocking and it lay folded on the tops of her unpolished black marching boots. The woman smiled broadly and embraced Róisín warmly.

"Darling," she said in an almost theatrical upper class accent, "I expected you yesterday. There is much work to be done. I have been ordered to leave for a safe house early tomorrow morning. Come. You and your young friend must join me for luncheon."

"Madame, this is Gráinne, a dear friend of mine from Wicklow."

"I am ever so delighted to meet you, Gráinne. You are indeed welcome to Surrey House."

We walked down a short passageway. Madame called out, "Bridie, Ellen, darlings, Róisín is back and she has a young friend from Wicklow with her. Could you please set two extra places for luncheon."

Madame explained that Ellen provided sustenance to all friends of Ireland who resided or sought refuge in Surrey House. Poor Bridie cleaned up the infernal mess that was left behind. We moved into the kitchen where four more boys, also uniformed but younger than those outside, were seated at the kitchen table looking at maps. When Madame walked in, they stood to attention and saluted. Ellen placed a large pot of tea, fresh buttered soda bread and a selection of cold meats on the table. When I had finished eating, Madame suggested that I might like to meet her daughter, Maeve, who was in the back garden. I made my way out the back door into what could only be loosely described as a back garden. Maeve, a pretty young girl about my own age, was seated on a wooden bench, her head buried in a hard-covered book. On her knee was a contented spaniel. I stood awhile in silence waiting for her to acknowledge my presence.

"I apologise," she said finally, looking up from her book. "Please excuse my manners. My name is Maeve. This little chap is Poppet. What is your name? Are you a friend of mother's? Do you know that grandmother had to buy this house for her or she would have nowhere to live? She spends all her allowances on the poor of Dublin. As a result, she never has a brass farthing for herself. When I arrived here last Tuesday, the gas had been turned off. She could not pay the bill. That night we had to read by candlelight. Father could stand it no longer and returned to the Ukraine with my step brother, Stasko. I do miss them. Cassie said that he longed for the old days when their home wasn't full of people agitating for some political or social cause. They used to live a life of gracious ease and pleasure, but now, due to her reckless generosity, we live almost like the people that Mother is trying to support.

"Maeve, darling, would you run upstairs and fetch the flag?"

Madame was now standing at the back door with Róisín. Maeve returned a few minutes later with a flag and laid it out on the grass. Róisín was wildly excited.

"This is indeed a proud moment. It's wonderful, truly wonderful. Where did you get it?"

"Mother made it last night," answered Maeve. "She just appeared downstairs with a green bedspread. We started painting the flag but the gold paint dried up, so we had to moisten a tin of powdered mustard to allow us to print the words "Irish Republic".

Madame walked forward and, without uttering a word, rolled up the flag and took it back inside. Róisín followed while Maeve announced that a friend in Charleville Road had invited her to afternoon tea. She went upstairs to change. I sat down on the bench and picked up the book Maeve had been reading. In fact, it was not a book at all, but a report. It was a copy of a secret intelligence report dated April 11th, 1916 detailing the activities of all the rebel factions operating in Ireland and was written by Major Ivor Price (Chief Intelligence Officer), Dublin Castle. The report was addressed to General Sir John French, British Home Forces. It was over two hundred pages and stated that while the Irish were, in general, loyal to the crown, the Sinn Fein Volunteers were running training camps and he was of the opinion that a rebellion was quite likely.

I put the report down and closed my eyes. I don't know how long I slept, but it was dark and I could hear Róisín calling my name.

I ran into the kitchen totally unprepared for what I found. The house had been transformed into a military headquarters. The carpets in the hall and reception rooms had been rolled up, exposing the floor boards. There were people everywhere. A large map of Dublin lay open on the kitchen table. Madame and Róisín had been joined by another young man and a woman. Róisín introduced me to Dr Kathleen Lynn and Con Colbert.

"Dia dhuit." Con smiled as we shook hands. This unexpected use of the Irish language and the fact that he was dressed in a military jacket and kilt took me completely by surprise.

"Yes, another Con," he said. This one is not nearly as important though. Are you a friend of Maeve's?"

"No, my name is Gráinne. I arrived from Wicklow this morning with Róisín. Are you a member of the Citizen Army?" I enquired.

"No. I am a drill instructor and council member of the

Fianna. I joined when I was thirteen, six years ago. Madame organised a recruitment meeting in the "Fianna Hall", Camden Street, looking for boys "willing to work for the Independence of Ireland". It sounded interesting, so I went along, joined and have been a member ever since. We were young, confused and bored. The Fianna gave us direction. We had to promise to work and establish independence for Ireland and never join the English armed forces. During the holidays and at weekends, Madame brought us to her cottage in Three Rock and taught us how to shoot. We began with Winchester rifles, then service rifles and revolvers. It is very important to know how to carry, handle and clean guns. Dr Lynn taught us first aid."

All of a sudden we heard a commotion coming from the back garden. Con ran out to investigate. Madame, Dr Lynn and Róisín instinctively ran into the hallway. Róisín beckoned me to follow her upstairs. I followed her up to the third floor, my heart thumping. We ran into the room over the kitchen where the young Fianna boys had been storing medical boxes. The room was in complete darkness and filled with the smell of disinfectant. When my eyes had adjusted to the dark, I could just make out wooden trestle tables piled high with sheets, blankets, medicines and thousands of rolls of bandages. On the floor, neatly stacked, were canvas and wood stretchers. Róisín quietly lifted the sash window, looked out into the garden and, after exchanging a few words, turned and declared that the disturbance had been caused by a drunken Citizen Army messenger with a dispatch for Madame falling over the back wall.

In the kitchen, Madame was reading the dispatch in silence. It was obvious from the expression that the news was good. The messenger, his eyes puffed and bloodshot, stood expressionless in the corner awaiting further instructions. Madame looked to the heavens and spoke.

"Last night, Eoin MacNeill of the Irish Volunteers was informed of the Military Council's plans for the Rising next Sunday, April 23rd. As you know, MacNeill, a pacifist, has continually refused to support an armed struggle. At eight a.m. this morning,a copy of a letter originating from Dublin Castle was delivered to his home. The Castle Document, as it is known, is a forgery and contains fictitious orders instructing the British Army to arrest all Volunteers. MacNeill has continually stressed the right to resist any attempt by the British forces to disband or confiscate arms, but he has also questioned the viability of a rising on the premise that the Volunteers would not be suitably armed. When he was informed of the pending arrival by sea of arms and ammunition in Kerry, he pledged the support of the Irish Volunteers."

Madame folded the dispatch, saluted and disappeared upstairs. The Fianna returned to their duties. The drunken messenger snored contentedly in the corner. Róisín went back upstairs to assemble medical kits. Maeve returned from her tea party and went to bed. Con and I retired to the drawing room to discuss the proclamation.

The Republic guarantees religious and civil liberty, equal rights, equal opportunities to all its citizens, and declares its resolve to pursue the happiness and prosperity of the whole nation and of all its parts, cherishing all the children of the nation equally.

It was now just after eleven o'clock. I was exhausted and fell asleep in a floral-covered easy chair. The last thing I heard Con say was:

Signed on behalf of the Provisional Government.

SATURDAY APRIL 22ND

Voices in the kitchen and hall woke me just after six a.m.. Slowly, I eased myself out of the chair, drew back the curtains and looked out the front window. The Fianna were still holding their positions at the gate, but two Dublin Metropolitan Policemen were crossing the road making for Surrey House. They inquired what everyone was doing up so early.

"A message has just arrived from Sligo. Mrs Gore-Booth has taken ill. Madame must travel home immediately," replied one of the Fianna.

I went out into the hall and noted that during the night the house had been cleared of medical kits and stretchers. As I entered the kitchen, Madame was filling a leather document case. She was no longer dressed in ragged civilian clothes but in a splendid military uniform: dark green woollen tunic with brass buttons, green tweed knee breeches, black stockings and heavy marching boots. On her head she wore a black hat with a plume of cock feathers. Ellen and Bridie were making sandwiches and Róisín was ironing her tunic. The back door opened and a little curly-haired boy, no more than twelve, announced that both the provisions and medical supplies had been loaded into Madame's car. The door behind me opened. Maeve walked in, bleary-eyed. Madame dismissed the Fianna from the kitchen. Slowly and deliberately, she scanned the occupants of the room. After acknowledging each individual with a reassuring smile, she gathered herself together.

"Women of Ireland ... You may ... You may ..."

Madame hesitated and took a deep breath. She was moved. Her lip quivered. The barriers were falling. She struggled to fight back the tears and failed. As the first tear eased down her cheek, she ran and embraced Maeve.

"I love you Maeve. ... Heaven knows I have not been a good mother ... I am a coward in the eyes of God. I stand ashamed, pleading guilty and begging forgiveness. I fear not the British rifle, but the thought that ... should I fail to return ..."

Madame took Maeve's hands, kissed each palm, composed herself again and continued.

"Rest assured that we shall not return until Ireland has been declared a Republic."

Silhouetted by the street lights, Madame disappeared down the lane behind the house. A powerful engine soon spluttered into life and, with its lights extinguished, Madame's car moved away in the direction of Grosvenor Square.

The Dublin Metropolitan Policemen on duty outside Surrey House enjoyed an unexpected pleasure. Hot cups of tea and freshly baked soda bread were presented on solid silver trays by Ellen. I went over to the range, poured myself a cup of tea and sat alone examining the contents of my tea cup, trying to piece together the complexities of events that culminated in the Rising planned for tomorrow morning. While the Volunteers appeared to have a common aim in establishing Home Rule and in removing the English from Ireland, some wished to achieve it through peaceful means. Others, like Madame however, had tired of this method and believed that the only way to succeed was through an armed struggle.

The back door opened. Con walked in. He looked drained.

"Would you like a cup of tea?" I enquired, standing up.

"Yes, please. I'm exhausted," he replied, collapsing into the fireside chair next to the range.

"Where have you been? Have you been out all night?" I questioned.

"I was over at Watkins Brewery. I am stationed there tomorrow," he answered, his eyes weary and worried.

While I made tea and buttered slices of soda bread, I asked Con to explain the build-up to the rising and how all the different parties linked.

"The Volunteers were formed three and a half years ago. Their aim was to defend and govern national rights, liberties and affairs. Within a year, they had almost 180,000 members. When war broke out in Europe, John Redmond, leader of the National Volunteers, reacted by pledging the party's support to England and the allies. This outraged many, including Eoin MacNeill, an officer in the Volunteers who initiated the formation of the Irish Volunteers. Jim Larkin, founder of the Irish Transport and General Workers Union, had already formed the Citizen Army. Its aim was to protect the Union members from the Dublin Metropolitan Police, who acted with particular brutality against them during the Lock Out. Larkin went to America and was replaced by the more aggressive James Connolly. The Volunteers were now split into two factions. MacNeill continued the Volunteers policy to seek Home Rule by peaceful means, refusing to take up arms unless the British government moved to disarm or disband them. Within MacNeill's Irish Volunteers were extremists led by Pearse, who was also a member of the secret organisation called the Irish Republican Brotherhood (I.R.B.). These men were convinced that only an armed struggle would result in the formation of the Irish Republic.

"'Bloodshed is a cleansing and sanctifying thing. There are many things more horrible than bloodshed and slavery is one of them,' Pearse said.

"When war was declared in Europe, the I.R.B.

approached the German authorities requesting guns and ammunition, which are due to arrive in Fenit Harbour later today. The Germans see their contribution to the Rising as a means of distracting the English while they are at war with them. The success of the Rising depends on the active involvement of the Irish Volunteers, the Citizen Army and the I.R.B.. In order to get their co-operation, the I.R.B. kidnapped Connolly, informed him of the Rising and convinced him to abandon his plans for a workers' revolt. Madame spoke last night about the Castle Document. This document is a forgery, created to induce MacNeill to join the Rising. It contains fictitious orders to arrest and detain all Volunteers. The conditions MacNeill stated would encourage the Irish Volunteers to join the Rising. The purchase and pending arrival of the arms from Germany further convinced MacNeill that if a rising was to be necessary then, even though heavily outnumbered, at least they had guns and not sticks."

This was the last time I spoke to Con. Exhausted, he closed his eyes and, before I had placed a blanket over him, he was asleep.

It was another lovely day so I went for a long walk down Charleville Road and into Rathmines. I arrived back at Surrey House just after eleven to find Maeve climbing into a trap. She was content now and had obviously found comfort from her conversation with Madame this morning.

"Good-bye, Gráinne," she said. "It was very nice meeting you. When this nonsense is over, you must come down to Lissadell to visit. November is a good time. We can ride to hounds. You do hunt, don't you? Do write if you get a chance."

I assured her I would write and visit Lissadell. We hugged and she was gone.

Inside Surrey House, Con had left for work and Róisín

was reading the Irish Times. I took the opportunity to explore the house and its wonderful contents. There were books and antiques everywhere. I was marvelling at a book of pen and ink drawings by Aubrey Beardsley when Bridie called Róisín and I into the kitchen. Ellen had prepared lunch. We had a leisurely lunch talking with the Fianna boys. Ellen told us about the old days when the Count and Countess spent endless nights entertaining in their house in Rathgar.

"This, of course, was before she got involved in the struggle," Ellen pointed out.

After lunch, Róisín and I were making our way upstairs when we heard a car pull up outside the house.

"My God!" declared Róisín, looking out the window. "It's Madame. Something's wrong!"

With that, the hall door burst open and Madame rushed in demanding that everyone make their way to the kitchen. Róisín was ashen-faced.

"Noble friends," Madame announced. "Word has just come from Tralee. The German arms ship, The Aud, arrived at Fenit Harbour ahead of schedule and was captured by the British. Its captain, rather than allow the arms to fall into the hands of our common enemy, scuttled the boat. Not alone have we lost the arms and ammunition, but we may now also lose the support of the Irish Volunteers. Obviously MacNeill, who agreed to join the Rising pending the arrival of arms, may now withdraw his support. Despite this setback, the Military Council have requested that I inform you that the Rising will go ahead as planned tomorrow morning at noon."

The support of the Irish Volunteers was essential to the success of the Rising. This loss of support would be deeply felt. Madame, observing the mood of her dejected supporters, boldly retorted:

Comrades we must wait until somebody gives us the word,
that will send us to Freedom or Death.
As free men defiant, we would sooner fall,
than be slaves to our dying breath.

She lingered for a moment, then broke into song:

Bless thou our Banner, God of the Brave,
Ireland is living, shout we triumphant.

Then she was gone. Róisín and I sat down at the kitchen table. I picked up the Irish Times and started to read an article entitled "Irish Nonsense Talked in Ireland" by Bernard Shaw. It was a reprint of an article he wrote for the New York Times. A strange article. I got the distinct impression that he was availing of the opportunity to ridicule from afar his fellow countrymen. Róisín meanwhile sat in silence, staring blankly at the wall. I had almost read the Irish Times from cover to cover before she finally spoke.

"Gráinne, I have been thinking about tomorrow. Earlier, I suggested you go with Mrs Connolly and stay in Three Rock, but I don't suppose that is what you want to do, … is it?"

I shook my head.

"It is now necessary for somebody to remain here in Surrey House to redirect orders and answer queries. If you are happy to stay on, I will contact Liberty Hall and inform them of your posting and ask them to dispatch two Fianna to help fetch and carry dispatches."

I was delighted and honoured that Róisín should consider me responsible enough to carry out this task and agreed without hesitation.

Róisín went out into the hall to phone Liberty Hall. I

watched her tall, angular body as she spoke on the phone. A lady dressed in black came in the front door and greeted Róisín in a strong Scottish accent. She came down into the kitchen and introduced herself as Lillie Connolly. I must have looked confused because she explained that she was James's wife and had called for Poppet. Róisín came in behind Lillie and informed me that two Fianna had been dispatched from Liberty Hall and would be with us within the hour.

Róisín spread out a vast array of papers on the kitchen table.

"Come along, Gráinne. Sit down. There are a few things I must explain. These are the official Military Council orders for tomorrow's Rising. At noon, the Volunteers and the Citizen Army under James Connolly will march from Liberty Hall and seize the G.P.O. and establish the Provisional Government. The plan is to occupy strategic points in a ring around central Dublin. Anti-clockwise, the main locations are the Four Courts, the Mendacity Institution, South Dublin Union, Jacob's factory, St Stephen's Green and Boland's Mill. The Cumann na mBan and the Fianna will act as messengers, nursing orderlies and stretcher bearers. You will see that under each heading there is an analysis of the command structure by location. All communications are to be addressed and dispatched to the relevant military commander."

My gaze was averted by the sight of two young Fianna vaulting athletically over the garden wall. Róisín stood to open the back door. She introduced them as Conor and Séan. They embarrassed me by saluting. Róisín instructed them to take up positions at the front and rear of the house. When they left the kitchen, Róisín sat down, took my hand in hers and said,

"Gráinne, I am not at all happy. On reflection, it was

really very irresponsible of me to bring you here to "Surrey House". You are but a child and I had no right to draw you into this Rising. I should have left you in Mountclare where you would be safe."

"Do not blame yourself Róisín," I said. "It was my decision, not yours, to walk through the Door to the Past in Mountclare. I am here of my own free will and curiosity."

"I sincerely hope I do not live to regret this," concluded Róisín as she gathered up her papers. Without uttering another word, and with tears now rolling freely down her cheeks, she pulled the rope tight on her tartan duffel bag and marched out the back door into the night.

I was alone for the second time since I had walked through the door on Wednesday. Was it only three days ago? So much had happened, so many new experiences. Little things like the real taste of Jersey milk, butter and cream. Larger ones like trams, Guinness barges and steam trains. The most astonishing was the poverty. Nothing could prepare you for the sight of starving, barefooted children standing aimlessly around street corners. I understood how Madame had become the guilt-ridden product of her class and why Róisín had found consolation in her crusade.

With the wind picking up outside, I dropped a few logs into the fire box and relaxed back in the fireside chair. I picked up a book left open on the arm of the chair, "Cuchulain, The Hound of Ulster". I got as far as Queen Maeve instructing her charioteer to slay the fairy maid when I fell asleep.

SUNDAY APRIL 23RD

"Gráinne, Gráinne, … wake up. There's a phone call for you."

I looked at my traveller's watch. It was seven a.m..

"It's Miss Róisín calling from Liberty Hall," Séan said.

My second night in Surrey House, I thought as I pulled myself up out of the chair, and both spent sleeping in an armchair. Róisín, despite the commotion in the background, sounded unfriendly and somewhat agitated.

"Gráinne, I am in a great hurry. There is a problem. Send one of the Fianna down to Rathmines to buy the Sunday Independent."

The phone went dead. I sent Conor down to buy the Independent. He returned within minutes. We placed the paper on the table and scoured its contents. There it was - an announcement by Eoin MacNeill and the Irish Volunteers:

Owing to the very critical position, all orders given to the Irish Volunteers for tomorrow Easter Sunday are hereby rescinded. No parades, marches or other movements of Irish Volunteers will take place.

Séan thumped his fist on the kitchen table.

"MacNeill withdraws his support, and chooses to place the notice in a capitalist newspaper. The man has cancelled the most important Irish Rising."

Séan was shaking with anger. The phone rang. This time it was Madame.

"Gráinne, the official word is that MacNeill has chosen to cut the ground from under our feet and the council are meeting at the moment to consider what form of action to take. We will keep you informed."

Séan, an introvert and the elder of the two, was devastated. He stared blankly into a cold mug of tea. Conor meanwhile talked freely about the cause, but mostly about Madame, whom he adored. Séan, shaking his head in bewilderment and anger, read MacNeill's announcement over and over. At one o'clock the phone rang again. It was Róisín.

"Gráinne, the Military Council have decided that manoeuvres are to be put back twenty-four hours. There are advantages; Monday is a Bank Holiday and at midday the streets are unlikely to be crowded. The city dwellers, weather permitting, will have abandoned Dublin to spend the day in Bray, Dalkey and Dun Laoghaire, many of the British soldiers will be in Fairyhouse for the races. This will leave the city not so well guarded. Our intelligence estimates that the British army strength on Monday will be no more than two thousand soldiers with one hundred officers. We anticipate that our forces will be in excess of fifteen hundred. If MacNeill had not withdrawn the Irish Volunteers, we would have expected a turnout of not less than five thousand. You should receive within the next half hour copies of the proclamation and detailed orders. These orders will be collected and distributed throughout the country by the Cumann na mBan. Gráinne, make sure when the new orders arrive you put them away securely. If they should get into the wrong hands at this juncture, it could further jeopardise manoeuvres. There is a hand-painted tile of a swallow in the kitchen over the range. Remove this tile and you will find a cavity in the wall. Conceal all documents there.

"I apologise if I was short with you earlier. Mr Connolly had just raised the Irish Flag over Liberty Hall. Some of the other Union members objected strongly and only relented when Mr Connolly threatened to resign. His daughter, Nora, is in Dublin at the moment with some friends. They will be staying with you in Surrey House tonight."

As I put down the phone, Conor came into the hall. The papers had arrived from the Military Council in Liberty Hall.

From about three o'clock that afternoon, various members of the Cumann na mBan called to collect orders, among others Maire Perolz, who had been ordered to Cork, Eily O'Hanrahan to Enniscorthy and Nancy Wyse Power to Carlow. To avoid detection, they were dressed as war widows.

At seven, Nora Connolly arrived with four girls dressed in nurses' uniforms. I had prepared cheese and homemade chutney sandwiches earlier. Conor made a pot of tea, and Séan cut up a fruit cake he found in the pantry.

"It is the first time that I have seen Dad cry," Nora told us. "He said that if there wasn't a Rising it would disgrace our generation, we had better pray to God for an earthquake or tidal wave. He then put on his uniform buckled his sword belt and sang."

We've got another saviour now ...
that saviour is the sword.

When Nora heard last night that the Rising had been cancelled, she rushed down from Coalisland on the early morning train. On her arrival in Dublin, she went straight to Liberty Hall to see her father, James. Nora was pleased to be informed that the Rising had not been cancelled, but merely postponed for twenty-four hours. She was annoyed that her fifteen-year-old brother, Roddy, was planning to march on the General Post Office alongside his father.

Nora was working for the Red Cross and the uniformed girls with her were members also. While I sat listening to the girls talk around the table, I became aware of the fact that I had not just gone back in time, but I had stumbled into another world. Here were four girls no more than eighteen offering their lives for their beliefs more freely than I would make my mother a cup of tea on Mother's Day. At that moment, I was deeply ashamed and at the same time proud that these women were Irish and willing to lay down their lives for their beliefs.

MONDAY APRIL 24TH

The next morning at eight a.m. I hurried downstairs to fix breakfast. To my disappointment, I found that Nora and the girls had left. Séan informed me that they had made their way down Leinster Road at six thirty a.m.. I was annoyed that I had missed them. I wanted to wish them luck but, more importantly, to tell them just how much I admired them. I stoked up the range, warmed my toes on the oven door and sipped a cup of tea. It was odd, I thought, sitting alone in the kitchen. The majority of Irish people refused to support the Rising. Indeed, they looked upon it as the work of madmen. For the first time in history, the Irish had full time employment from the British Army at war in Europe and the many service industries that supplied it. It was quite understandable that the public would look upon these rebels as crazed animals, gnawing away at the hands that fed them.

"Miss Gráinne, come quick. The Constabulary have returned," called Séan from the hall.

I went to the front door and, right enough, two Dublin Metropolitan Constables were standing menacingly at the front gate. This was unusual; they usually observed from the shelter of the oak tree across the road. My instincts told me something was not quite right. I went through the kitchen and out the back door to find Conor to see if he had seen anything out of the ordinary. As I opened the kitchen door and called Conor's name, I heard a muffled shout, a shuffling of feet and saw two constables moving along the back wall. Their cover broken, the order was given to "Take the house!".

At that instance, five or six of these huge men vaulted over the wall. I ran inside, bolted the kitchen door and, in the second it took me to cross the room to the range, I thanked God that I had loaded the fire box earlier. With my hands shaking uncontrollably and my heart trying to burst out of my blouse, I removed the tile, withdrew what was left of the Military Council orders and the proclamation and deposited everything in the fire box. The Constabulary at the front, when they heard their colleagues attempting to break down the back door, set about the front door with axes and sledge hammers. Séan ran into the kitchen to help destroy the documents. I motioned to the fire box. He opened it and was relieved when he saw that the papers were burning. But the ashes were starting to extinguish the flame. He called out to me. I was frozen to the spot. All I could hear was the Constabulary noisily grunting and groaning as the wood in the kitchen door splintered. Séan ran into the scullery and emerged with an oil lamp. He removed the wine-coloured globe, cutting his hand as it broke into sharp slivers of glass. Angrily, he hurled the offending globe at the back door, turned to the range, opened the fire box and poured the oil onto the smouldering documents. The back door finally gave way and three burly constables fell in a heap on the floor. Outside the window, two constables were climbing up the drainpipes. I could hear them smashing the window frame in Róisín's bedroom. Meanwhile, at the front door, a large hand was poking through the shattered glass looking for the bolt restraining the door. I looked towards the range. Not alone were the papers ablaze, but so too was Séan. He was in grave danger. I ran into the laundry to get a damp blanket. Suddenly, I was swept off my feet by a burly constable. He carried me into the study and handcuffed me to the leg of a bookcase. Outside in the kitchen, I could hear Séan roaring obscenities at the policemen as they extinguished the flames.

"You silly Fianna scoundrel. We should let you burn,"

roared one of the constables.

"Allow me to die and it will be to my eternal glory and to your shame. I pledge to Ireland my love and I pledge to the supporters of English rule our hate," replied Séan.

The door of the study opened. Séan's head appeared. He was bundled into the room, hands cuffed behind his back. One of the policemen burst in. Unprovoked, he raised his baton, then smashed it into Séan's knee cap. As Séan fell forward in pain, another police constable came from behind, formed a fist and punched him between the shoulder blades. Séan collapsed on the floor.

"You may break my bones, but never my spirit!" Séan exclaimed.

Séan and I were imprisoned in the study, one police constable guarding the door, another standing at the bay window outside. Escape was impossible. Upstairs, room by room, the house was being systematically searched and destroyed. Madame's antique furniture was reduced to kindling. Her father's magnificent rolltop writing desk that for centuries graced the panelled study in Lisadell House now lay crumpled on the front lawn. Madame's clothes were hurled from her bedroom window along with her books, paintings, papers and ornaments. The only thing that they could neither break up nor throw out the window was a printing press, which was carried out the front door and placed on the back of a flat truck.

"We must escape," whispered Séan. "If we don't, we will be dispatched to Kilmainham prison or, worse still, a mental asylum."

Something caught Séan's eye. He moved closer to the window. His eyes narrowed. He was communicating with somebody using sign language outside the gate. After a few moments, he nodded and turned away from the window.

"The Fianna," he whispered, "have left two bicycles

under the oak tree across the road. When the word is given, you must mount the bicycle and head for Rathmines. When you get to the library, turn and go round to the back of the Town Hall. The Constabulary will expect us to head out of Dublin and make for Madame's cottage in Three Rock."

"When did you learn sign language?" I enquired.

"My younger brother, Padraig, was born deaf and dumb. When he was five, he was sent to the School for the Deaf in Donnybrook. He was taught sign language and Catechism by a young sister from Arklow who had been sent out to Boston to train. Communicating with Padraig at home meant that in a short time all the family had learnt how to sign. When Padraig joined the Fianna, I thought it would be a good idea if the boys learned sign language, too. It helped Padraig and improved communications on manoeuvres."

Outside, a large, curious crowd had gathered. The door to the study opened and two policemen walked in. One removed Séan's handcuffs and dragged him to his feet by his hair. The other unlocked and removed my handcuffs and, in total contrast, helped me to my feet. As he walked me to the hall door, he enquired as to whether I was Madame's daughter. I did not answer. I was focusing on making my escape. As we reached the gate, the crowd opened up to allow us pass. As swiftly as it opened, it then closed around us. I was lifted off my feet and propelled from behind across the road towards the oak tree. A young freckle-faced boy stood holding a big, black gentleman's bicycle. With great difficulty, I mounted the rusty bike and pedalled towards Rathmines. I dared not look back. At the library I stopped and was relieved to see Séan about thirty yards behind, pedalling furiously. In the distance a group of policemen ran towards us. Behind them a police car was trying to make its way through the crowd. Séan roared at me to follow him. The yard and outbuildings behind the Town Hall were deserted. We hid the bicycles in the overgrown grass and rested in the loft over the coach house.

We waited for almost ten minutes before making our way back up Rathmines Road. We had decided to take a tram into O'Connell St and, from there, walk down the quays to Liberty Hall. At least we may be of some value there.

As we crossed over at the library, a troop of about fifty Volunteers in ten rows of five came marching down Leinster Road. They were quite obviously members of the Citizen Army and in a great hurry too. Séan saluted as they passed. I could not help but think that perhaps MacNeill was right when he said, "The hapless Volunteers are attempting to fight bullets, armed with Rosary beads. The only justification for an armed rebellion is a widespread discontent."

Listening to the Volunteers being ridiculed as they passed it was apparent that, in Dublin in 1916, if there was discontent in British occupation, it was not at all evident on the streets.

When they reached the library, the officer in charge ordered his command to halt. He crossed over to the Town Hall, glanced firstly at the clock and then up and down Rathmines Road. He returned to the library and ordered his men to split into groups. He positioned ten men on the steps of the Town Hall, ten more up Leinster Road. The main body retreated behind the library. Minutes later, the Rathmines tram appeared, rattling down Rathmines Road. As it came to the corner of Leinster Road, the command was given. The Citizen Army rushed forward, halted and boarded the tram, then ordered the irate passengers off. The driver was instructed to make haste to Liberty Hall. As the tram began to pull away, Séan took hold of the handrail and jumped on the platform. As he did so, the officer moved forward to prevent him from boarding. Séan beckoned me to follow and saluted.

"Fianna with a dispatch for Mr Connolly in Liberty Hall, sir."

The tram ride took no more than ten minutes. We found Madame and Róisín in an office on the third floor of Liberty Hall.

"What the devil are you two doing here? You should be in Surrey House. Séan, this is really not good enough. Explain yourselves this instant," exclaimed Madame.

"We are sorry, Madame, but the Constabulary raided Surrey House two hours ago. There was nothing we could do. We were arrested. They didn't get any documents; we burnt them. The Fianna helped us escape by causing a diversion as we were led from the house. Unfortunately, we think that they may have arrested Conor."

"Conor is only a juvenile," Madame said. "If he has been arrested, he will be released when his identity is established. I will make arrangements, however, to secure his release immediately. Róisín, take these young Volunteers to the canteen. In the meantime, we will decide what best to do with them."

Róisín led us downstairs through a labyrinth of passageways to the canteen. It was filled to capacity with hundreds of impatient men, women and children. The Cumann na mBan were busily dispensing tea from large urns. Thick cheese sandwiches were piled high on large trestle tables covered in delicate lace tablecloths. Séan told me that the tablecloths came from Madame's family home in Sligo.

The tension in Liberty Hall as noon approached was coiled. Some Volunteers laughed nervously. Others stood in silence, their brows furrowed and damp. All observed the

Smith's wall clock with concern.

At twenty minutes to twelve, a young red-haired girl informed us to report to Madame's office. As we left the canteen, the formidable figure of James Connolly approached. Mr Connolly was of medium height with a dark, bushy moustache and was impeccably turned out.. He was of a heavy build and perhaps a little overweigh, but he was indeed a powerful figure in his uniform and polished leggings. As we reached the top of the stairs, thunderous applause and cheering erupted from the canteen and we could clearly hear the "Soldier's Song" echoing around the corridors below.

"Séan, I have arranged for you to join Con Colbert in Watkins Brewery. Gráinne you will travel with Róisín, Doctor Lynn and me. Our orders are to distribute medical supplies. Go now with Róisín, collect Doctor Lynn from the supplies office and wait for me at the car."

Séan saluted Madame first, then Róisín. I offered my hand. He ignored it and, instead, wrapped his two muscular arms around my waist and whispered, "Good luck, Gráinne. Please be careful. I haven't known you very long, but I would like to call you my friend."

I hugged him tightly, then kissed him on the cheek. I was annoyed that I could not think of anything sensitive to say. The truth was that I had grown very close to Séan and, at this moment, was quite distressed. I tried to speak, but I just gurgled. I hoped he understood.

The car was parked opposite Liberty Hall. Clouds of cigarette smoke floated in the still air. Hundreds of men and women in uniform circled nervously. Some had fixed bayonets, others polished rifles and handguns. Their uniforms were as diverse as the people who wore them. Some arrived in suits, but most wore a green military jacket of sorts with a badge, cap and bandoleer. They carried an

80

assortment of weapons: rifles, shotguns, picks and pikes. The pikes were used to cut the reins of mounted soldiers. The Cumann na mBan and Red Cross nurses loaded stretchers, medical kits and endless rolls of bandages into an assortment of carts, buggies, lorries and cars. While all this activity was going on, the Dublin Metropolitan Police observed.

"First Battalion Volunteers for the Four Courts, fall in, Second Battalion Volunteers for Jacob's Factory make ready."

One by one the various battalions came into line and, on the sounding of the bugle, proudly marched into the unknown. Madame appeared just after James Connolly departed with his men for the G.P.O.. Madame mounted the running board and eased herself into the passenger seat of the car. Doctor Lynn whispered to Róisín as I tried to find somewhere to sit amongst the medical supplies.

"You would be well advised when Madame takes the wheel to sit back and take a firm hold."

Madame, Róisín explained, had only recently learned to drive and had not quite mastered the technique. I could testify to this an hour later when Madame crashed into a street lamp while frantically waving her hat to a company of Volunteers. The drive to City Hall, where Doctor Lynn was to set up a field hospital, brought us along by the Custom House, down the Quays, around Trinity College and up Dame Street past the Olympia. As we neared City Hall, Madame turned and said, "Gráinne, you see before you Dublin Castle, the embodiment of seven hundred years of British tyranny, a machine for governing Ireland against her will."

The car shuddered to a halt outside City Hall. There was a heated confrontation at the main Castle gate. Madame dismounted, spoke to a friend of hers, Helena

Maloney, then ordered us to stay with the car. About twenty members of the Citizen Army had surrounded a tall grey-haired police constable. An officer of the Citizen Army was remonstrating with the constable.

"That is Séan Connolly, the famous Abbey actor," Róisín informed me as a soldier behind the constable levelled his rifle at Séan Connolly. The constable pushed the rifle aside saying, "It is a lovely day, men. Can you not go and annoy someone else? We do not want any trouble here."

Connolly's small thin frame moved menacingly forward to confront the constable, who began to close the gate. Connolly's voice quivered in anger.

"Stand back man and open these gates."

A gun shot rang out. The police constable lay on the ground, half his head blown away. For a moment everyone, including the soldier, stood motionless. Another constable came running around the corner. Helena raised her revolver and shot over his head. In that moment, she saved the man's life. The constable, quickly assessing what had happened, ran for cover. I was ill, my stomach wretched and I began to tremble. Róisín brought me across the road and sat me down in a doorway. This was the first time I had seen a dead body, or what was left of it. When they placed the constable on a stretcher and carried him away, they left half the unfortunate man's head on the pavement.

Róisín and Madame unloaded the medical supplies. I watched in a trance. Ten minutes later we departed City Hall, leaving Doctor Lynn to set up her field hospital. Madame took the wheel of the car and we headed back along Dame Street, around by Trinity College, and up Grafton Street to Stephen's Green, the largest city square in Europe. Barricades were being busily erected on nine of the ten approach roads. Stephen's Green, a public park of twenty-two acres, is known simply as the Green. Inside the railings, men in shirt sleeves were digging deep trenches. As we approached the grand entrance arch known as Traitors' Gate, another dead police constable was being removed by stretcher. The arch was erected to the memory of the Royal Dublin Fusiliers who died fighting the Boers in the British Army. While I watched, the ambulance disappear down Grafton Street. A young woman came up to Madame and informed her that the Chief of Staff, Michael Mallin, had issued instructions that Madame was to report to him on her arrival.

Madame headed off towards the Shelbourne Hotel while Róisín and I carried the medical supplies into the Green. They were to be stored in the Summer House. The supplies in place, we had a refreshing cup of tea and a salty ham sandwich. Before we had finished our tea, Madame reappeared with a small troop of Citizen Army soldiers.

"Róisín," Madame said, "Due to the poor turn out of Volunteers, the Chief of Staff, Mr Mallin, has appointed me Lieutenant. I am now second in command with orders to patrol the Green. Róisín, I want you to …"

A shot rang out, the bullet coming from the direction of the Shelbourne Hotel. It lodged in a tree next to the Summer House. In a split second, Madame had removed her handgun from its holster, dropped to one knee and returned fire. Instinctively, I fell to the ground, my head covered by my hands and buried in the freshly mown grass. I lay motionless, my eyes firmly closed.

"Got him!" said Madame triumphantly.

Madame ordered me to report to the bandstand, where the field hospital had been set up. My function was to maintain and control stock of medical supplies. Róisín and Madame set off to patrol the Green. On my way to the bandstand, I took a closer look at the barricades. They contained everything from trams and cars to hat stands and kitchen tables. One had a laundry van, another a dead horse. All were wired together for strength. As I passed one of the gates, two men with fixed bayonets and rifles and a third with a handgun ran past me, out of the Green and into the roadway.

An expensive car drove up Dawson Street. The young man with the handgun, his face sun burnt and grimy with dust and sweat, courteously addressed the chauffeur and the solitary male passenger seated in the rear.

"Pardon me, gentlemen. We are commandeering this vehicle on behalf of the Irish Citizen Army."

He opened the door, requesting the irate passenger to dismount. He then ordered the bewildered chauffeur to position the car in the barricade. This done, the three Volunteers retreated. As the chauffeur joined his employer on the steps of the Shelbourne Hotel, a man emerged from the crowd and crossed over to the barricade. He gripped the shafts of a cart lodged in the centre. As he did so, five armed Volunteers standing inside the railings demanded that he move away immediately. The man held his ground and slowly eased the cart out of the barricade. Three shots were fired over his head. The man ignored the command and, instead, calmly and arrogantly walked over to the Volunteers. He informed them that it was his property and he had no intention of leaving it behind. They warned him again to return the cart to the centre of the barricade or he would be a dead man. He persisted.

"Go before I count to four," shouted an officer.

"One, Two, Three, Four."

A single rifle shot rang out. The man was killed instantly. One woman ran up the street screaming hysterically while another sat on the pavement and wailed. The man was placed on a stretcher and carried away. As he passed, I saw the hole in the top of his head where the bullet had entered.

Madame, hearing the shot, ran up the street to see what had happened. When she saw the dead man, she cursed and called for the soldier who had killed him.

"This man is a prominent member of Sinn Fein. The man who shot him will be court-martialled immediately."

I was mentally and physically ill and vomited into a storm drain. My head was spinning and my legs were shaking uncontrollably. I could not come to terms with the fact that in the last two hours I had witnessed three Irishmen being violently murdered by Volunteers, supposedly fighting for an Irish cause.

At the top of Grafton Street, the driver of a car risked the lives of his two male companions and himself by ignoring a command to position his car in a barricade. A young man with savage eyes, no more than twelve years of age, came forward, raised his revolver, pointed it at the driver, then fired a single shot into the car tyre. The car was promptly driven on the rim to the barricade. Another man tried unsuccessfully to remove his motor bike from a barricade. I stood awhile behind the railings. Beside me, a young Volunteer was being verbally abused by a group of angry women. He tried to defend himself.

"A starving man who steals a loaf of bread is sent to prison, while a rich man who steals a Nation's Liberty is sent to the House of Lords."

All around, civilians were standing on corners and in doorways, staring in total disbelief. Many boarded up broken windows and doors. In the Shelbourne, privileged guests, who earlier drank tea and sipped cocktails, now began to take the developments a little more seriously as the Volunteers took control of the Green. Their safety was in question as stray sniper bullets began to find their way into the hotel. When I arrived at the bandstand, Nellie Gifford was directing two Red Cross nurses attending to a distressed Volunteer with a bullet wound in his shoulder. Through the railings I could see Madame talking to a group of young men. I moved over to hear what she was saying.

"In this supreme hour, under the protection of God most high, rise and declare your right to control your destiny … Your reward shall be a Sovereign Independent State … For your pains you may expect a bullet or a rope around your neck."

One of the Citizen Army ran over and interrupted Madame. Annoyed at the intrusion, she reluctantly turned and spoke to the young man, then looked to the rooftops where he was pointing. Madame carefully studied all four corners of the Green, then turned on her heels and made off in the direction of Grafton Street. As she passed, I heard her say to Róisín, "I have requested an immediate meeting with Mr Mallin in the summer house."

I made my way over the humped bridge, past the bandstand, duck pond, through the many wondrous flowered walks and on to the summer house. Stephen's Green at that moment was an oasis. The sun shone brightly, the ducks circled searching for crumbs and playful magpies teased an angry tomcat. When I arrived at the summer house, Mr Mallin, Róisín and Madame were deep in conversation. I stood behind Madame while she spoke.

"Mr Mallin, I estimate behind the railings there are but one hundred men and eleven women Volunteers. At the moment, the British army are moving snipers into positions all around the Green. By tomorrow morning, when reinforcements arrive, we can expect up to one thousand British soldiers to command the rooftops. From these vantage points, there is every chance that the Volunteers will be massacred. I am of the opinion that if we remain in the trenches we will be remembered as martyrs who dug their own graves. We require a line of retreat. I suggest that we move now and take the College of Surgeons on the west side of the Green."

Mr Mallin stepped back to survey the splendid Georgian buildings that surrounded the Green. As he did so, a short burst of fire came from the direction of the United Services Club. Mr Mallin fell to the ground clutching his head. Madame ran to his side and turned him on his back. Mr Mallin shook his head and sat up. Madame, relieved, picked up his cap, which had been dislodged, and handed it back, her right forefinger sticking through the hole the sniper's bullet had just passed through.

"Madame, your observations are correct. Take a small party with Sergeant Robbins to the north end of the Green and, as you suggest, commandeer the College. Beware, though, of the caretaker. He is a rabid Unionist and will do everything in his power to prevent you taking the building."

Madame selected three men and with Róisín and Sergeant Robbins set off for the College. I followed to the front gate, then monitored their progress from behind the railings in the Green.

When they arrived at the front of the three storey College of Surgeons, Sergeant Robbins observed that the caretaker was talking to a Fellow of the College. Grasping the opportunity, he lunged at the door. The caretaker reacted by firing a single shot from a handgun through the door. Sergeant Robbins, with his boot wedged in the door and his revolver aimed at the caretaker's head, forced open the door and arrested the caretaker. I ran out of the Green past the statue of Lord Ardilaun and crossed the road to the College.

As I arrived, Sergeant Robbins was questioning the caretaker. Over his head on the wall was a copy of the Ulster Covenant. Madame enquired of the caretaker what it was. He replied that he had never seen it before. She then asked him the whereabouts of the College armoury. He mimicked that in all the years he had been working there he had never come across such a thing. Madame, for the caretaker's safety, ordered that he be locked in his rooms with his wife and family.

We climbed up on the roof where Madame raised the tricolour. This was the signal to abandon the Green and commence fortification of the College. For the next two hours, under spasmodic fire, we carried ammunition, provisions and medical equipment from the Green to the College.

The Rising was now gathering momentum. Flames appeared in the skyline all around the city. The intensity of gun fire and the number of locations it came from increased dramatically. It was clear that the limited number of British Army snipers who had taken up positions around the Green earlier in the day had been reinforced and become more aggressive. It was also evident that we were surrounded.

The bandstand was now strewn with bodies of wounded men. Some bore their pain in silence, others wailed disturbingly and cursed the heavens. At its base, prisoners sat in silence next to the motionless bodies of their dead comrades. The transfer of medical equipment to the College had severely depleted our stock of bandages. I made my way over to the summer house. When I arrived, I looked at my watch. It was midnight. A Fianna was informing Madame and Róisín of how the Rising was progressing in other parts of the city.

"The General Post Office was taken and the tricolour raised at noon. Patrick Pearse duly read the Proclamation on the steps. Later, the G.P.O. was charged by Lancers based in Marlborough Barracks. They retreated swiftly, though, when two of their mounted soldiers and four of their horses were killed under Nelson's Pillar. Séan Connolly was shot this afternoon. He was raising the flag over City Hall when a sniper put a bullet in his head. They are saying that he was the first Volunteer to kill and be killed. His young brother, Mathew, was with him. British Soldiers are taking up positions all around the city. Reinforcements from Athlone, the Curragh and Belfast have arrived and are also moving into position. Further troops from England are due by sea early tomorrow."

I gathered up as many bandages as I could and ran back to the bandstand. I arrived as a young Fianna, his features almost completely obscured by blood, was dying. I could see that he had been shot in the neck and that the blood cascading from the wound was choking him. He gasped for air and tried to speak, but only managed to gurgle. The young nurse attending him was trying unsuccessfully to stem the constant flow of blood. She was helpless and, as a result, abandoned her composure and began to cry uncontrollably. He gathered all his strength and tried to sit up. When he managed, aided by the nurse, even in this semi-darkness I could see the terror in his eyes as they darted from left to right, aimlessly searching for a way out of this nightmare. Suddenly, he became aware of my existence and fell silent. Slumped in the nurse's arms, he narrowed his eyes and tried to focus on me through the blood and sweat that stung his eyes. His features, which had been tense and contorted, now became relaxed. He smiled as if in recognition, sat upright and beckoned me to his side. Nervously, I began to walk in his direction and, just as I was about to lean over to offer comfort, he gave one long gasp and fell back limply into the nurse's arms. The blood flow that she had spent the last hour trying to stem had stopped, ... like his heart. She lay his head gently on her lap. The tears that now fell freely caressed and exposed his face to the moon. She gently wiped his face with her apron, looked up to the stars, closed his eyes and whispered.

"Séan, you have found eternal peace now. Return to your maker triumphant."

A voice said, "Be careful Gráinne, my friend. I love you. Be careful."

TUESDAY APRIL 25TH

I awoke Tuesday morning to the sound of two women discussing the fact that they had spent the night sleeping on the cold floor of the summer house while Madame had slept in the comfort of Doctor Lynn's car. It took a few moments to register whether or not what happened last night was a dream or reality. From the sound of the shooting outside the summer house where I lay, it was evident that fighting had intensified considerably. Without any consideration for my safety and oblivious to the heavy rain, which overnight had replaced the glorious sunshine, I ran across the Green to the bandstand looking for the girl who had nursed Séan the previous night. While I prayed that Séan was alive, my heart told me he was dead. The bandstand was now partially covered in a green tarpaulin, protecting its few remaining occupants from the rain driving in from the North. Inside, Nellie Gifford was attending to a civilian who had cut her hand on some broken glass. She looked up.

"Gráinne, isn't it?" she queried, then continued, "How are you feeling? ... You passed out last night. Róisín had you carried over to the summer house. We gave you something to help you sleep."

"Is Séan ... dead?" I asked nervously.

The look on her face answered my question. What I did not know was that the nurse who had comforted Séan was killed herself barely ten minutes later by a sniper positioned on the roof of the Shelbourne.

"Gráinne," Nellie brought me back to reality. "Róisín left instructions that you are to relocate to the College of Surgeons. We moved the field hospital over earlier this morning. During the night, the British Army set up a machine-gun on the roof of the Shelbourne and over one hundred soldiers were counted in Dawson Street. We could not possibly defend the Green with so few men. The final orders to retreat are to be issued shortly. Go now, while there is a lull in the shooting. Follow the trenches to the main gate and cross over at Grafton Street."

Distraught, confused and up to my ankles in mud, I forged my way through the trenches. As I crossed over at the main gates, I viewed a commotion in Grafton Street. On closer inspection, I saw that the shop windows had been smashed and looters were hurling themselves dangerously through the splintered plate glass. Young children were running up and down the street, their pockets, hands and mouths filled with toffees, chocolates and boiled sweets from Noblett's sweet shop. Others paraded in bowler hats, silk scarves and trilbies from Morgan's. Their elders went for more expensive goods. Two old beggar women passed with a hand cart laden with silk bed linen and lace tablecloths. Four men manoeuvred a huge mahogany dining table up the street. Behind them, a small pony pulling a wooden cart was led by a barefoot boy no more than five. His cargo - the matching dining chairs. Everywhere, men, women and children squabbled over fur coats, cocktail dresses and tweed suits. In South Anne Street, a group of boys were playing cricket, the wooden stumps wedged into a storm-drain cover. One enterprising man laid a blanket on the ground and was selling gold watches, charm bracelets and diamond rings. Another, on the opposite side of the street, was trying to sell a huge crystal chandelier. Open season had been declared. The Constabulary had been withdrawn and the British Army were more concerned with the rebels. A woman was trying to exchange a ring with the man selling the jewellery on the blanket. From O'Connell Street, the sound of heavy artillery could be heard. A man next to me said that a gun ship was at the bridge along with several armoured cars and they were firing shells at the post office. The atmosphere, which earlier was carnival, was now hostile. The public houses were being attacked. Bottles of whiskey and barrels of Guinness ran into the streets and were consumed greedily. I was enthralled by the pure theatrics being acted out on the streets. I was also becoming nervous and headed back up Grafton Street, carefully picking my way through the debris.

The college was unrecognisable; the windows and doors had been smashed and barricaded. I could see Madame on the roof with two other marksmen. They were shooting in the direction of the Shelbourne and a sniper in an abandoned tram. When I arrived at the door, a shot rang out and a bullet hit the masonry next to my head, the grit rebounding into my eyes. As I pounded on the door, the rat tat tat of what I knew to be a machine-gun came from behind. The bullets crashed into the concrete at my feet, creating a cloud of dust. The door opened and a tall young man with a strong pair of arms dragged me inside. He informed me that I should hurry as there was a meeting in the basement. Numbed, I picked my way downstairs in the dark. I caught sight of Róisín standing on the podium. The white marble slabs that lined the walls of the mortuary were being dismantled and carried upstairs for the injured. When I arrived at the bottom of the stairs, I could contain myself no longer and ran to Róisín. All the fear and emotions that I had been bottling up for nearly a week exploded in one outburst. I could not talk, only sob. Embarrassed I ran from the room and up the stairs. Róisín caught me within a few strides and tried to comfort me. I was inconsolable. Madame appeared on the stairs, shouting instructions in every direction. When she saw Róisín and me, she stopped, put her hand on my shoulder and declared,

"Séan was a brave young Irishman, a distinguished Fianna soldier and, more importantly, a good friend. Gráinne, there is no greater glory than to die for your beliefs. Be proud that you were one of the few Séan called a friend."

From the basement a beautiful male tenor voice sang:

Conquer we must when our cause is just,
and this be our motto, in God we trust,
and the Tricoloured Banner in triumph shall wave
over the land of the free, and the home of the brave.

Madame retreated to the basement. As she entered, the room went silent. I remained with Róisín on the stairs. Madame relayed to the one hundred or so Volunteers present the content of the many dispatches that had been received to date. More importantly, she deciphered the fact from the fiction in the rumours emanating from the streets. Mr Mallin informed us that all strongholds, while under heavy fire, were holding fast - except for City Hall. Séan Connolly was dead and, with a greatly weakened unit, Dr Lynn had been forced to surrender. The British Army had dissected the city and were moving heavy artillery, machine guns and armoured cars into position.

As all the buildings surrounding the Green were terraced, Mr Mallin ordered tunnels to be dug through all interior walls from York Street to King Street.

"Should the British Army mount an attack on the College, then these tunnels would provide an additional and welcome means of retreat," he declared.

"The Rising had been a success," Mr Mallin continued. "There can be no humiliation now. The British Army have paid us the highest compliment by introducing heavy artillery. Ireland's honour has been redeemed."

Triumphantly, Madame held up the current edition of the Irish Times, which contained nothing other than a copy of the proclamation. The headline read:

Evilly disposed people have disturbed the peace, but the situation is in hand.

In contrast, Mr Mallin read from the Republican newspaper, The Irish War News.

Republican Forces everywhere are fighting with splendid gallantry. The populace of Dublin are plainly with the Republic.

The meeting concluded. The Red Cross nurses collected up their medical kits and, along with the Cumann Na mBan, headed off in various directions, some to the kitchens, others to distribute ammunition. Róisín and I followed Madame up to the roof of the College. It was raining heavily and the surface was slippery. It was a different world here, high above the wet cobbled streets. There was a network of walkways linking the roofs, making it possible to walk with little difficulty from one end of the Green to the other. The large chimneys and balustrades on the roof gave excellent cover. I felt quite secure helping Róisín to load the ammunition for Madame. The two young snipers crouched beside her.

Down below on the street, a dead horse was being stripped of its bridle and harness by a young boy. Close by, three bodies lay motionless, two on the street, the other lying on a park bench inside the Green. The man on the bench was alive, but only just. He lay face up, his limp, lifeless body mercilessly pounded by the heavy rain. An arm hung lifeless, pointing to the ground. Blood trickled down his arm, circled his wrist, then dripped from his forefinger to the gravel underneath the bench. The door below opened and a party of three Volunteers, one carrying a stretcher, another a white flag, dashed across the road in the direction of the Green. Madame and the other Volunteers on the roof commenced cover fire, but before the three men reached half way across the road, two lay dead, cut in half by the British machine-gun posted on the Shelbourne. Two more brave lives lost. The third was now standing beside the man at the park bench. He had just gripped the wrist of the dying Volunteer to check for a pulse when two rifle shots came from the direction of the University Club, The third rescuer, like his comrades, lay dead, his head resting in the pool of blood still trickling from the hand of the Volunteer on the bench. Within seconds, their blood had merged.

At three thirty, the din, which had been steadily growing since early morning, reached a new level when the boom of heavy artillery could be heard exploding all around the city. This carried on relentlessly until dark when the Dublin skyline glowed red - not with the promise of fair weather, but with the flames from a burning city.

WEDNESDAY APRIL 26TH

Wednesday morning at daybreak we were back on the roof. Another machine-gun had been set up by the British Army during the night. this time on the roof of the Stephen's Green Club. In the early morning light, I could see that the dead bodies had been removed from the Green. Small children ran around searching for war souvenirs in the mistaken belief that they would not be targeted. A burst of gunfire from a British Army sniper left one young girl, no more than eight years old, wounded in the leg. She sat frightened and bewildered on the footpath. A young accomplice ran to drag her to safety. Another burst of gunfire left the young boy dead. The bullet that exploded in his chest pierced his heart. He died instantly.

Before we had time to come to terms with another senseless murder, Margaret Skinnider, a Scottish friend of Madame's, came out on the roof requesting permission to take two men and burn out the sniper who had fired upon the children. Permission granted, Margaret and her party left the College and made their way towards the building from which the sniper was firing. The footpath sparked all around them as they wove their way towards the building. The machine-gun on top of the Shelbourne opened fire,. Two Volunteers, one of them Margaret, fell. The other ran for cover in a doorway. Margaret was alive. The young boy, about Séan's age, was dead. Under heavy covering fire, ordered by Madame, Margaret was recovered and the mission aborted.

Down below in the street, a flat-back lorry with "Dublin Zoo" crudely hand-painted on its side winched up the dead horse and carried it away.

On every street corner, despite the unending stream of

bullets, crowds stood and observed. We were now under siege; additional firepower had us pinned down. Bullets were crashing into the walls. Brick and cement dust was everywhere. Despite this, an elderly woman with four young children gripping her skirts called to the rear entrance of the College at lunch time with milk, sandwiches and biscuits for her grandson.

The word from the street was that all positions were holding firm. The G.P.O. was still under the control of the Volunteers despite being subjected to continual artillery fire and the fact that the rest of O'Connell Street has been virtually razed to the ground. The British Army was reported to have opened fire on the Metropolitan Fire Brigade attending to the fires. Madame returned to the roof and informed us that Margaret was badly wounded but would, thankfully, survive.

Later that afternoon, Róisín and I crawled downstairs into the College. The relative calm we witnessed earlier had been replaced by bewilderment and fear. As the battle raged inside and out, the nurses of the Red Cross and the Cumann na mBan, with little regard for their own safety, acquitted themselves with a bravery and self-sacrifice worthy of the finest tradition in Irish nursing. Their heroism was not confined to the College, but out on the streets, too, attending, under fire, to the dead and wounded.

That night, the sound of artillery, rifles and machine-guns never ceased. Smoke and dust reached from the ground to a sky that sparked and still glowed red. Despite everything, I was calm. The last thing I heard before I fell asleep was an old Volunteer remarking to Mr Mallin that, "The Irish have always gone bravely into battle, but unfortunately they have always fallen, too."

THURSDAY APRIL 27TH

We awoke yet again to the bitter sounds of battle, louder and, if possible, more intense than before. We had slept in the exam room, which had been converted into the field hospital. All around, the pitiful sights, sounds and smells of the dead and injured abounded. A young man of maybe sixteen years lies moaning in fear and pain on a cold marble slab, his shoulder and part of his ribcage blown clean away. All this suffering for a cause he could not possibly understand. Beside him, a young girl, a nurse, her uniform stained by blood and sweat, fruitlessly picks the remaining shattered bones from the cavity that yesterday formed his chest. This unfortunate young man is waiting in semi-darkness to die, bravely enduring a pain that will only subside with death - the only cure for all ills. He will take with him a clean soul for he was not shot in anger, but by a cruel twist of fate. The old Lee Enfield rifle borrowed from his father had accidentally discharged while he was cleaning it.

On the roof, Madame was talking to Mr Mallin. She was certain that the British were planning to storm the College. The barricade at the top of Grafton Street was ablaze and dead civilians lay on the paths and roadways. A grey-haired old man lay in a pool of blood that completely encircled his body and was inching its way towards a storm drain. Dublin was on fire, smoke and flames billowed everywhere. A pretty young Cumann na mBan girl appeared on the roof requesting an audience with Madame.

"Madame, when I left last night with your note for Mr Connolly, I was followed by the military. I first noticed them behind me as I walked down Grafton Street. As I turned the corner into Suffolk Street, I ran, but they called out to two soldiers who were coming down Andrew Street. I hadn't a chance and they arrested me."

"Did they get the note for Mr Connolly?" Mr Mallin enquired.

"No sir, I swallowed it. It nearly choked me, too. But when they didn't find anything, I was arrested and marched to Trinity College. The Sergeant brought me up to the old library and made me strip in front of four other officers. They laughed and joked while a nurse carried out an internal examination. I was cold, wet and humiliated, but they did not break my spirit. "

"How old are you, Dáire?" Madame queried.

"Just fifteen, Madame," the girl replied.

"You are indeed a brave young woman and, make no mistake, your bravery and dedication will not go unrewarded," said Mr Mallin. "What other news have you for us?"

"The General Post Office is still in the hands of the Volunteers, but it is now under constant bombardment from the Naval Gun Boat, "Helga", moored at the bridge. The exterior walls are standing, but the roof is badly damaged. O'Connell Street has been levelled, fires rage everywhere and only about one third of it remains standing. The army will not allow the fire brigade to tend the fires. They are hoping to smoke the Volunteers out of the Post Office. At eight o'clock this morning, Liberty Hall was destroyed by the "Helga". Nobody was injured."

"The Helga was built by Irishmen in 1908, only to return to kill Irishmen in 1916," Mr Mallin observed.

The Cumann na mBan formed the backbone of the Rising. In most cases, unarmed and alone, they defied the same dangers and bullets as the Volunteer soldiers. Each day, without regard to their safety, they took to the streets and parks carrying dispatches, ammunition and explosives while snipers aimed rifles at their hearts.

All day, and into the night, the fighting raged. Later, as I approached the stairs leading to the boardroom, a shell scored a direct hit on one of the barricaded windows to the front of the College. The large hole inflicted by the shell opened up the College defences. Instantly, a grenade came in through the opening. A Fianna, who had been crouched against the wall alert to the danger, lunged forward, took the grenade in his hand and hurled it back out into the night. Watching the grenade explode with such ferocity made me mindful that, while his actions were brave, they were also foolhardy.

The cavity inflicted by the shell was hastily filled by a bookcase and a mahogany dining table from the boardroom. The excitement abated. The sound of singing filled the College. It came from the direction of the Gallery room. I climbed the stairs. The door was ajar. Seated in a circle on the floor were about twenty men and women singing, "Wrap the green flag around me.". On the floor beside them were empty tins of Bourneville Cocoa and Bland's Health Salts. They were making primitive bombs. Around the walls on shelves were a variety of specimen jars filled with human brains, kidneys and hearts. Behind me, an elderly man came shuffling down the corridor calling out for Mr Mallin. He had three rifles suspended over his head. He proudly declared that he had found the College arsenal: ninety rifles with ammunition.

This news was dampened later when we received word from the G.P.O. that James Connolly had been shot.

FRIDAY APRIL 28TH

I could not sleep. The isolated bursts of gunfire continually shook me from my slumber. Inexplicably, I lay in the dark, my head buried deep under a rough woollen army blanket, my hands clasped tightly between my knees. I had been frightened before, but this was different. I became tense and coiled in anticipation. I understood how men and women under fire could act completely out of character.

The dawn of another sunny day was a welcome relief. Dublin was on fire. On the far side of the Green, perched on the roof of a red brick Georgian house, a group of men and women, a white flag raised, fought to prevent their home being burnt to the ground. The men aimed fire extinguishers and hoses at the flames. Women and children had formed a chain and passed along buckets of water. They were losing the battle, much to the obvious delight of the British soldiers, who commenced firing on them from the roof of the Shelbourne. A small party of the soldiers exited the hotel and ran towards the front door of the burning house. At the bottom of the steps leading to the hall door, they stopped. A soldier came forward and tossed a grenade onto the top step. It exploded, reducing the hall door to matchwood. They disappeared up the stairs. On the roof, the fire was now raging out of control and the debris was collapsing in on the floor below. A uniformed arm reached up through the smoke and removed the white flag. Seconds later, the flag was in the hand of one of the soldiers as he and his comrades made their way back towards the hotel alone.

Madame cursed, raised her rifle, took careful aim and fired a single shot. The soldier with the white flag fell. We watched in horror as all the floors began to collapse. Still, nobody appeared to make their escape. A young woman appeared at one of the windows on the second floor. Her dress was on fire and her arms were tied behind her back. She raised her foot and kicked the sash window. The glass fell out into the street. She looked at the flames raging behind her, then down at the street thirty feet below. She made her choice, then eased herself on to the window ledge and fell. I turned away.

In the space where the front door had been, a little boy and girl stood motionless holding hands on the step. The woman, perhaps their mother, lay dead like a crumpled rag doll.

Dead and injured dogs and cats were everywhere, target practice for wearied soldiers.

Through the railings, circling the Green, I could make out a middle-aged man walking from the direction of Leeson Street. As he rounded the corner at Harcourt Street, I could see that in his left hand he held up a white flag made from an old faded cotton vest. It was tied to the handle of a broomstick. Holding on to his right hand was his young daughter, oblivious to the dangers surrounding her. Mother walked behind, carrying their worldly possessions wrapped in a black woollen fringed shawl. From the barricade at Grafton Street, an English officer withdrew his revolver and moved forward to interrogate them. The man released his grip on the child's hand and reached into his coat pocket. The officer levelled his revolver and fired. The man fell to the ground, pinning his frenzied daughter beneath him. His wife collapsed on the pavement. The officer and two soldiers ran forward and, after establishing that the man was dead, rolled him off the delirious child and then abandoned him face down on the road. In his left hand, the man held his Dublin Metropolitan street pass.

A Fianna handed Madame a dispatch from Mr Pearse.

She read aloud:

*The forces of the Irish Republic, which was proclaimed in
Dublin Easter Monday April 24th, have been in possession
of the central part of the capital since 12 noon on that day.
Up to yesterday afternoon, headquarters was in touch with
all main outlying positions and, despite firing and
continuous assaults by the British forces, all those positions
were still being held and all the commandants in charge
were confident of their ability to hold them for a long time.*

Madame, unconvinced of the accuracy of Pearse's fine
prose, enquired of the Fianna who had delivered the
dispatch, "Truthfully, young man, how stands the G.P.O.
this fine morning? Be mindful that the flames and the
smoke are clearly visible from here."

"Madame, the truth is the roof and upper floors of the
G.P.O. are on fire. The sky is exposed down to the ground
floor and the Volunteers have retreated to the basement.
This morning, I overheard Mr Connolly and Mr Pearse
making plans to abandon the G.P.O."

Madame held up Mr Pearse's dispatch and declared that
this was indeed an inappropriate time for Pearse's poetic
phrases.

"We need a man of military competence, not a poet!"
she shouted.

Madame sat down on a pile of bricks. Below on the
streets and on the roofs surrounding, the British soldiers
were inching their way ever closer to the College. A baker's
van, with a red cross crudely painted on its side, turned into
the Green and stopped at the entrance to Grafton Street.
Two men dressed in white coats jumped from the back of
the van and knelt at the body of the man shot by the officer.
They walked across the road to where the man's wife sat

motionless, supported by the park railings. They examined her for a few moments, then gently laid her down on the footpath and called for a stretcher. Two soldiers ran forward and placed her on the canvas stretcher. One of them bent down to retrieve the woman's black shawl. He placed it over the woman, covering her head. They made their way back to the ambulance. The woman had not collapsed, but had been shot in the back. Her worldly possessions, which had been wrapped securely in her shawl, lay on the footpath where she died.

Madame removed her hat and ran her fingers over the plume of fine cock feathers. It seemed that the firepower which had been directed at the G.P.O. was now redirected at us. She was powerless, surrounded on all sides, and incensed. Madame deliberated, then ordered Róisín and I to withdraw from the College the following morning. We were to travel to her cottage in Three Rock and make ready to accommodate the main party of retreating Volunteers on Sunday.

SATURDAY APRIL 29TH

Róisín and I did not sleep at all on Friday night. Outside, the British could be clearly heard shouting, cursing and banging on the walls of the College with their rifles. At five a.m., tired and weary, Madame came down from the roof to speak with Mr Mallin. She felt certain that the British were preparing for a bayonet charge. She had observed armoured cars and troop carriers being moved into position behind the smouldering barricades at Harcourt Street and Grafton Street. They discussed at length Madame's suggestion to retreat to Three Rock.

At noon, a Fianna informed us that the British Army had re-taken the G.P.O. and that the Provisional Government had, within the hour, surrendered. He informed us that O'Rahily had been shot dead trying to escape. He found him in Sackville Lane, his head propped on a curb stone, his feet spread in a doorway. He saw a woman pull her Red Cross emblem from her blouse and place it on his chest..

Mr Mallin's decision, much to Madame's consternation, was to continue to hold their position.

The mood in the College was sombre. It was a time for reflection. Now that the romance had been hacked away and the adrenaline had stopped flowing, the realities of war began to register. Over seven hundred and fifty Irish men, women and children were reported dead and almost five thousand injured. What had been achieved? Indeed, what did they ever hope to achieve? Day became night and, with it, the reality that the Rising was over. All through the night, groups of people assembled to pray for the dead and living. The comfort found in prayer became more important with the advent of new fears. The treatment of Irish political prisoners by the British was well-documented. The best an Irish citizen tried and convicted could expect was to die of disease and malnutrition in a remote English gaol, the worst to face a firing squad.

Madame, who had long abandoned her religion but was now courting the likelihood of death, was deeply moved by the apparent inner strength the Catholics were deriving from communal prayer. She knelt at an altar erected to the Blessed Virgin Mary and joined in reciting the Rosary. Inspired, she returned later with her own prayer to the Virgin Mary.

Your silvery voice, soft as a dying breath,
was answered by a hundred loud and clear,
craving a grace from her whom all hold dear.
Mary be with us at the hour of our death.

"I greatly regret my lack of faith," Madame admitted. "For the first time I see no future. Everything I can see of this world is current. That which is unseen is eternal."

Sunday April 30th

Sunday morning, while artillery fire was intermittent, the rattle of machine-guns continued. At fifteen minutes to ten, the city's church bells summoned the faithful to mass. They also heralded the arrival of a car driven by a British Army officer. Seated beside him was a young woman. They alighted from the car. The woman stood as the officer saluted and spoke to the soldiers at the barricade. The order to cease fire echoed around the Green.

Madame stood at the balustrades watching the officer and the woman slip from behind the security of the barricades, raise a white flag and walk slowly towards the College. Madame, tears streaming down her cheeks, turned away from the street and, avoiding eye contact, gathered up her ammunition and disappeared down into the College.

In the hallway, Madame spoke to the woman who arrived with the English officer. They were well acquainted. Róisín said she was Elizabeth O'Farrell, a Red Cross nurse and a leading member of the Cumann na mBan. The tall, thin British army officer, Major De Courcy Wheeler, stood defiantly rolling a cigarette in his mouth. His arrogant superiority angered a Volunteer beside me who raised his pistol and pointed it at the Major's head. Madame seized the Volunteer's hand and lowered it to the ground. The Major, a little less arrogant and decidedly shaken, hastily instructed that the Volunteers' arms were to be laid in the centre of the boardroom and withdrew immediately. We followed Mr Mallin and Madame to the Long Room. Mr Mallin sat at the head of the table, Madame at his side. His sombre face confirmed the fears of the assembled gathering of over one hundred brave men, women and children. His voice faltered as he spoke.

"I have sad news, comrades."

He ran his fingers through his thick brown hair and, while trying to regain his composure, nervously twisted his bushy moustache between his thumb and forefinger. He continued.

"Our leaders have issued orders to surrender. Mr Pearse has stated that, in order to prevent the further slaughter of unarmed people and in the hope of saving the lives of our followers, the Provisional Government have agreed to an unconditional surrender. We have been ordered to lower our flags and lay down our arms. I have here an endorsement from Mr Connolly. Both orders are dated April 29th."

There was uproar in the Long Room. Men and women cursed and demanded their right to refuse to surrender. Like Madame, they said that they had joined the Rising willing to die for their beliefs and considered the orders to surrender to be contemptuous. An elderly man, bursting with emotion, fought his way to the podium and called for silence.

"If we surrender, the British Army will put us to death. That being the case, I would rather die here on my terms than before a firing squad in Kilmainham gaol on their terms."

The room erupted in agreement. Mr Mallin rose and the hall fell silent again.

"I want to express my gratitude for your loyalty and bravery. It has been an honour to have been your leader. We came here as loyal soldiers abiding by the constitution of the Provisional Government and that is how we shall leave. This battle is over, but the war has just begun. Dead, you are of no benefit to the cause. Alive, you can carry it to the four corners of this proud land. As leaders, we can expect to be shot, but we swore our allegiance to the tricolour and will be proud to die for our beliefs. Many of you have family commitments. I order you to return to your families."

Mr Mallin saluted and marched from the boardroom. The meeting, like the Rising, had concluded. Madame, in animated conversation and racked with emotion, embraced Róisín in the knowledge that for her part in the Rising she would certainly face the firing squad. She ordered Róisín to leave the College and, as Mr Mallin instructed, "Carry the Battle". "Not just to this proud land," she said, "but to the world."

When Róisín and I exited the College into York Street, we were greeted by a group of angry men and women waving Union Jacks. As we reached the barricade at Harcourt Street, Major De Courcy Wheeler, who had delivered the terms of surrender, had returned to the College. This time he entered with a small party of armed soldiers. Róisín pointed to the roof of the College. Mr Mallin was lowering the tricolour. As he folded it, a small cortege of British Army vehicles parked at the corner of York Street and Mercier Street. A large boisterous crowd had now gathered to witness the surrender at the main entrance to the College on the Green. Róisín and I remained in York Street.

At two-thirty, the Countess Markievicz and Mr Mallin exited the College of Surgeons into York Street, followed closely by Major De Courcy Wheeler. Mr Mallin, unarmed, saluted the officer and handed over his walking stick. Madame kissed the barrel of her revolver and did likewise. The officer enquired if Madame would like to accompany him in his car to Dublin Castle. She refused, saying that her preference was to be with her own kind.

The formal surrender of the Volunteers completed, Major de Courcy Wheeler climbed up into his car and issued the orders to proceed to the Castle. Madame, with her slouch hat, knee breeches and green brass-buttoned

110

tunic, strode out proudly at the head of her men. We observed from a close distance, but retreated as the mood on the streets turned from curious to hostile. The Volunteers, initially subjected to verbal abuse from the people on the streets, were now under fire from stones, bricks and mortar - in fact, anything likely to cause injury.

The British soldiers fixed bayonets.

The short walk to Harcourt Street station would normally take about five minutes, but today the street was blocked with the remnants of the barricades, broken glass, cardboard boxes, paper wrappers, even mannequins thrown from a burnt-out clothing factory in Montague Lane.

We spent over an hour trying, unsuccessfully, to find a jarvey willing to take us to Madame's cottage in Three Rock. We decided to go to the bakery and seek advice from Delia.

The British army had already been to visit. The front door swung open on its hinges. Róisín called Delia's name. There was no response. The shop had been ransacked. There was a noise from the back of the shop. The door at the bottom of the stairs opened. Standing in the doorway was the young blind girl we encountered when we arrived off the Wicklow train. She was carrying a loaf of bread rolled in brown paper. She told us that Delia had moved to a house in Stamer Street owned by a firm of house painters called Macken. Within the hour, we were on our way to Three Rock in a four seater gig driven by Delia's son, Fergus. Delia owned a post office in Sandyford and Fergus's movements would not be questioned. It was imperative at this time that we not travel beyond the city boundaries as the British troops would arrest anyone attempting to leave the city without a Royal Irish Constabulary pass stamped by the District Inspector.

CHAPTER 16

The cottage at Three Rock was situated at the base of the Dublin mountains. Lillie Connolly, petite wife of James, and Poppet greeted us on our arrival. Lillie was delighted to see us and immediately questioned us on James's welfare. We informed her that he had been shot, but not seriously.

On Monday afternoon, the tranquillity in the cottage was broken by the headline in the Daily Sketch. It declared that James Connolly was a "Dead Rebel". Lillie was devastated. She was, of course, a realist and wholly expected the British reprisal to inevitably result in James standing before a firing squad. As Lillie made ready to return to the city, there was a knock on the door. It was her ragged and weary daughters, Nora and Ina. They had just returned from the North and, thankfully, were able to confirm that James was most certainly alive.

"Mother, gangrene has set in He may lose his leg, but he will not lose his life," Nora reassured Lillie.

Lillie raised her hand for silence.

"I remember the day England declared war on Germany. John Redmond, Chairman of the Irish Nationalists in Westminster, inexplicably and without authority swore Ireland's loyalty to the English Houses of Parliament. He could have proclaimed our benevolent neutrality, but instead he allowed his emotions to betray the people of Ireland. He is wholly answerable for the blood spilled during the insurrection. The English, in time, would have granted Home Rule in exchange for Irish soldiers. The newspapers reported this week from the War in Europe that the Dublin Fusiliers took on the might of the German Army and captured Hulluch. Irish fighting men are a commodity and the English know this fact all too well."

Tuesday morning, Nora and Ina set off for Dublin. They were to stay with a good friend of their father's, Bill O' Brien, a member of the Union and one of the three typesetters who printed the Proclamation.

The newspapers were full of reports by nameless special correspondents, informing us daily of life on the streets during and after the Rising. They offered us pictures and biased profiles of the treasonable leaders of the rebellion, endless accounts of their murderous activities and numerous analytical lists of casualties.

Late Wednesday night, Delia called with word that Patrick Pearse, Tom Clarke, and Thomas McDonagh, had been executed by firing squad at dawn.

"The British policy is not alone devious, but criminal. If they take a prisoner of war in Germany, they do not place him in front of a firing squad and shoot him for defending his country. They respect his courage. For centuries, Britain, the most powerful nation in the world, has persistently robbed and beaten the least powerful, ... Ireland. They will never break our spirit. We have become tenacious in hate, but anaesthetised against misery," said Delia.

Thursday morning at dawn Lillie, dressed as always in black, set off for Dublin. She had convinced herself during a sleepless night that she was travelling to James's funeral. On her arrival in Dublin, Lillie dispatched Ina to the Castle to visit James. The authorities confirmed he was alive, but refused to grant a visit. As Ina was leaving, she met a tired and drawn Father Aloysius. To her relief, he had spoken to James earlier.

"James is very much alive," he assured her, "but he is very ill. His comrades, unfortunately, are not so fortunate. This morning, the British provided us with four more

113

martyrs. They allowed poor Joseph Plunkett to marry Grace Gifford last night and, four hours later, executed him by firing squad along with Edward Daly, Michael O'Hanrahan, and William Pearse. The Countess was court-martialled earlier and condemned to death. The sentence was subsequently withdrawn, much to her disgust."

The news of these deaths was particularly disturbing. None of these men played any significant part in the Rising. Their executions were a statement of intent. Joseph Plunkett's was despicable. He was terminally ill with consumption and had only days to live. Róisín was deeply upset and pointed out that Joseph's execution meant that Grace Gifford and her sister, Muriel, who was married to Thomas MacDonagh, were widowed within twenty-four hours.

Friday afternoon, Nora and Ina called to visit. They informed us that John McBride, another who held no command in the Rising, had been executed that morning. Ina, who had spoken to Muriel Gifford that morning, chronicled an insight into the conditions the prisoners were suffering in Kilmainham.

"Thursday morning at one a.m., without notice, an army lorry pulled up outside Muriel's house. The officer in charge informed her that Thomas expressed a wish to see her. She was, of course, fearful of what this meant. When she was led into the cold, foul-smelling cell in Kilmainham Gaol, the same officer took out his pocket watch and informed her that she had ten minutes and suggested that she should make the best of it as it was to be their last together. Thomas was to be shot at dawn. Two soldiers, bayonets fixed, stood motionless in the damp cell. A single candle illuminated a decomposing rat, cockroaches and slugs. There was no bed, just a woollen blanket laid over a rough timber plank on the ground. There were two tin basins, one for washing, the other a toilet. Beside the bed was a three legged stool on top of which was a wooden food bowl. Its contents remained uneaten. The smell of urine and damp was overpowering. Despite all this, Thomas was strong. His last words were,

"Fear not for me, Muriel. All week I have stared down the barrels of British rifles. Today, those same rifles will bestow on me the honour to die for my country."

Saturday morning, without warning, Fergus appeared. It had been decided that it was now safe to travel and he had been detailed to drive us to Wicklow. In Enniskerry, he stopped to buy tobacco and a paper. The man in the shop advised Fergus to avoid the main roads around Bray. The Constabulary had sealed off the town and were searching for Volunteers.

The horse watered and fed, we set out following the back roads for Mountclare. The Irish Independent had no further news of executions, but the editor was clearly demanding more. The paper described those responsible for the Rising as "insane criminals". The letters page, however, was more moderate. It was apparent that the men and women on the street were not happy with the manner in which the executions were being carried out. The general view was that those who had been put to death did commit a crime, but they should have been considered prisoners of war and treated as such. Their subsequent slaughter was considered by some to be a crime of a equal magnitude to the Rising itself.

At four o'clock, we drove back through the gates of Mountclare. A group of sombre and highly inquisitive nuns shuffled down the steps to greet and interrogate Róisín. Fergus and I were directed to the kitchens for refreshments - tea and a wedge of fruit cake. Róisín was escorted to the dining room for afternoon tea. The kitchens were cavernous. The staff were preparing for supper. Eagerly, they twisted and turned, juggling with saucepans, plates and trays, somehow managing to avoid collisions. The kitchen was capable of producing and serving over two hundred meals three times a day. Fresh churns of milk and cream stood outside in the dairy to cool. Freshly baked cakes of brown bread were laid on a flour-drenched trestle table. Five chicken carcasses rattled in an enormous pot, boiling furiously on the range. Beside it, a saucepan of bubbling homemade apple jam.

Fergus finished his tea and announced that he was off to Quinn's public house in Wicklow town. He would return in the morning. Róisín appeared with the disappointing news that Sister Mary Francis was still on retreat. Her rooms were locked and she was due back on Thursday. Róisín suggested that I go and stay with a friend of hers who lived in Arklow.She would send for me when she found the Key to the Past.

Monday morning at mid day, Mrs Brennan's chauffeur, Pat, collected me as arranged at the train station in Arklow. We went directly to her home, "Saint Peter's". The open-topped Rolls Royce attracted great attention as we negotiated our way down the narrow Main Street, over the bridge and out the Wicklow Road. We were met at the gate by her jovial gardener, Jimmy, who directed me towards the large granite two-storey house overlooking the sea. I was formally greeted by Mrs Brennan in the entrance porch.

Mrs Brennan guided me through the elegant and expensively furnished house and out through the french doors on to the brick patio. Guarding a trestle table laden with every conceivable type of food and beverage were two housemaids dressed in black service uniforms. Though of different ages, their identical pattern of freckles and red hair deemed them sisters. Mrs Brennan invited me to select from the table. As I reached for a side plate, a wireless crackled into life behind us.

... Rebels executed. The following rebels were executed in Dublin earlier today: Eamonn Ceannt, Séan Heuston, Michael Mallin, and ... Con Colbert.

I was aware that Mrs Brennan was talking, but nothing registered. "Why, oh why?" I repeated over and over and over again. Michael Mallin was a professional soldier and served with the Royal Scottish Fusiliers in India.. He expected to be shot. Séan Heuston was in the Fianna with Con and could be no more than nineteen years old. To execute one impressionable and politically insignificant young man was a criminal act; two was a villainous war crime. I tried to imagine what it would be like to stand before a firing squad. I remembered what Fr. Aloysius told Ina last Thursday in Dublin Castle.

"They marched Mr Pearse into the yard, his arms bound behind his back, then stood him in front of a crumbling red brick wall. A soldier bound his ankles while the officer in charge unbuttoned and placed his hand inside Mr Pearse's jacket, determining the exact position of his heart. A piece of paper cut in the shape of a heart was then pinned to Mr Pearse's jacket and the hood placed over his head. In the darkness to his right, he would have heard the muffled sound of the priest praying for his soul, to his left, the officer ordering the firing squad to Make Ready, ... Aim ... Fire!"

In the College of Surgeons one night, Mr Mallin discussed with Madame an interesting theory on death by firing squad. Many believed that the sound of the bullet firing was heard after the bullet had actually entered and killed the prisoner.

Mrs Brennan, visibly distressed by the news, sat on a wrought iron chair next to the patio doors. I sat opposite. United in grief, we cried.

On Wednesday morning, Róisín rang and made arrangements for my return to Mountclare. That afternoon, refreshed but deeply depressed, I was delivered back to Arklow train station for the return journey to Wicklow. I had occupied my time in Saint Peter's deliberating on the beach and watching the British soldiers moving in and out of the ammunition storage depot at Kynoch. It was a rewarding two days that allowed me to gather and arrange my thoughts and feelings. The singular objective now was to return to Mountclare and retrieve the Key to the Past from Sister Mary Francis.

Mr Clarke collected me at the station in Wicklow. He was a man of few words, so the journey to Mountclare was in silence. At the gates of the school, he stopped to glance admiringly at his sign.

Róisín was alone in the kitchen when we arrived. Mr Clarke handed Róisín a small brown package. She motioned for me to sit while she placed a pot of tea and a plate of freshly baked fruit scones on the table. Róisín removed two mugs from the dresser, handed me the Irish Times and sat down. The headline read:

Thomas Kent executed.

When I looked up, Róisín was crying.

"Poor Con," Róisín cried. "I remember the day he first called to 'Surrey House'. He was only fourteen and very small for his age. He was working in a bakery and wanted to join the Fianna. In the following years, with Madame's help, he worked his way up to be a clerk in the bakery and an important member of the Fianna council. For what? To die a reluctant martyr?"

Róisín opened the brown paper bag Mr Clarke had handed her earlier. Inside were two identical keys. Róisín explained.

"On Monday night after supper, I was talking to Matron in the infirmary. One of the senior girls was rushed in. A teapot had accidentally fallen in her lap. Her arms and legs were badly scalded. Matron asked me to fetch liniment from the medicine cabinet. As I did so, a large bunch of keys fell to the floor. On closer inspection, to my delight, I recognised them as belonging to Sister Mary Francis. This morning, when Matron travelled to visit the orphanage in Rathdrum, I returned to the infirmary, removed the key to Sister Mary Francis's room and requested Mr Clarke to have a copy made in the hardware shop in Wicklow."

Róisín returned the master key to the infirmary, then informed me that we must locate the Key to the Past tonight as Sister Mary Francis was due back in Mountclare tomorrow morning.

Róisín suggested I rest awhile. I was exhausted and welcomed her proposal. She led me to her bedroom buried deep in the bowels of the school. It was almost how I imagined a prison cell: four damp and bare stone walls, low ceiling and cold slate floor. The only light came from a single oil lamp perched on the corner of a small bedside table. The bed ends were semi-circular and made of crude cast iron, not brass. Their use was functional rather than decorative. What little clothes she had were stored in a small wooden chest. A washstand with a recessed china basin and water jug was provided for washing. I climbed up on to the narrow, steel, coil-sprung bed, lay down on the lumpy mattress and slept.

Róisín woke me. It was nine o'clock and the nuns would be settling down for the night, she said. We made our way down the dimly lit passageway, back through the kitchen and up the stone steps to the ground floor. As we arrived in the reception hall, I slipped on the polished floor. Róisín put her finger to her lips for silence and indicated that we should remove our shoes. Down past the chapel we went, around the corner and up the stairs to Sister Mary Francis's rooms. The corridors were silent. Róisín fumbled nervously in her dress for the key. The rooms were in complete darkness. I stood by the door allowing my eyes to adjust to the dark. Róisín disappeared into the sitting room and commenced searching for the Key to the Past. The writing bureau, side board and display cabinet yielded nothing.

All of a sudden, there was a break in the clouds and moonlight flooded the room. Róisín returned to the bureau and eased herself into the leather button back chair. As she crossed her legs, something under the bureau caught one of her stockings. Róisín pushed back the chair and went down on her knees and began examining the underside of the bureau. There was a click and a drawer sprung out of the centre of the bureau. Róisín rummaged for a while. Then she stood triumphantly, holding the Key to the Past aloft.

We slipped back into the corridor. Róisín locked the door. Excitedly, we retraced our steps back to the warm silent kitchen.

"Gráinne, you must return through the Door to the Past tonight."

"Are you not returning with me?" I enquired.

"You must understand, Gráinne, I have made a new life here. It is easier for you to adjust to going back in time than for me to go forward. With all the leaders except for Mr Connolly executed and with Madame destined to life imprisonment, the cause is not yet won. There is much planning and work to be carried out yet."

Suddenly, the silence in the kitchen was shattered by the sound of horses galloping up the gravelled driveway. We sat transfixed as men's heavy walking boots climbed the stone steps and began pounding on the front door.

"This is the Constabulary. We have orders for the immediate arrest of Róisín Burke. Open this door or we will be forced to break it down. You have one minute."

Róisín sprung from her chair and removed the Key to the Past, draped around her long slender neck. She offered it to me along with a parcel from under the table.

"Run, but take this parcel!"

"What is in the parcel?" I enquired.

"It is the night-clothes you were wearing when I found you."

Outside a constable bellowed, "You have only thirty seconds left."

Róisín shook me by the shoulders and screamed,

"Gráinne, go quickly. When you return to the future, tell Clodagh I love and miss her. Please try and explain to her why I cannot return just yet, and be mindful not to reveal the secret of the Door to the Past to anybody."

We embraced as the Constabulary commenced attacking the front door with axes. Róisín pushed me roughly towards the stairs. Without looking back, I ran to the top of the stairs. I stopped for a moment as a large axe head sliced through the front door. I turned and ran down the corridor away from the Constabulary. I opened the door at the end of the corridor and entered the scullery where Róisín found me when I first arrived. I ran up the rickety wooden stairs to the Door from the Past. I placed the clothes parcel on the floor while I removed the Key to the Past from around my neck. I eased the key into the lock and turned it clockwise. The door creaked open. Behind me, I could hear shouting as the Constabulary made their way down to the kitchen. I stepped into the corridor opposite Sister Clodagh's room and locked the Door to the Past behind me. I could faintly hear the sounds of furniture being smashed and Róisín screaming. A light went on in Sister Clodagh's room. I remembered the clothes parcel. I had left it on the floor behind the Door to the Past. I was wearing day clothes from 1916. I had no choice - I had to return. I put the key in the lock and turned it. Nothing happened the key just spun around. With my hand trembling, I tried again. I could hear Sister Clodagh walking across the room to her door. This time the lock clicked. I turned the handle, removed the Key to the Past and opened the door. As I closed and locked the door behind me, I could hear Sister Clodagh's door open, but I could no longer hear Róisín. I bent down to pick up the clothes parcel. It was not where I left it. The stone floor was cold to my touch. The stone floor, I thought ? I came up a wooden stairs, not a stone stairs. I fell back awkwardly against the wall. It was made of rough stone. Curious, I made my way back down the steps. As I neared the bottom, I could hear strange voices. I opened the door slowly and squinted through the opening. What I expected to see was the corridor leading to the entrance hall.

Facing me was a man of about six foot. He wore a red silk jacket over a white silk shirt adorned with a ruby brooch worn at the neck, black pantaloons trimmed with gold brocade, white silk stockings and black laced square-toed boots. Beside him stood another man more elegantly dressed. He wore a yellow padded silk waistcoat over a white doublet sleeved shirt, with matching fringed pantaloons. His jacket was made of black velvet and trimmed with gold ties His square-toed shoes were tied with yellow ribbon matching his waist coat and pantaloons. Both men's faces were heavily made up and they wore matching curly blonde wigs. A distinguished looking young woman joined them. She was adorned in jewellery: gold chains, bracelets, earrings and rings that sparkled in the candlelight. Her dark brown hair was curled and sparkled with semi-precious stones. Her dress, of white silk, shimmered as she moved. The bodice was tight with a full skirt shaped over a farthingale. The neckline and hem were edged in the most delicate of lace.

The room was lavishly furnished and lit only by wall candles and a huge stone open fireplace. Surely I haven't passed further back in time, I thought. Then I remembered something Róisín had said to me when I spoke to her first.

"Mountclare Castle was burnt to the ground in 1660. The nuns bought the estate in 1710 and built the school around the remains of the old castle."